Men, Women, & Bridge

Startling Tales of the
BRIDGE TABLE

By RICHARD CRAWFORD

**With an Introduction
by ALAN TRUSCOTT**

STERLING PUBLISHING CO., INC.   **NEW YORK**

OTHER BOOKS OF INTEREST

Bridge Analysis   Begin Bridge with Reese

To Sylvia

Acknowledgment

The author and publisher wish to thank Sam Fry, Jr. for his advice and assistance in preparing this book.

Copyright © 1978 by Sterling Publishing Co., Inc.
Two Park Avenue, New York, N.Y. 10016
Manufactured in the United States of America
All rights reserved
Library of Congress Catalog Card No.: 77-93316
Sterling ISBN 0-8069-4934-1 Trade
4935-X Library

Contents

Introduction

by ALAN TRUSCOTT

Bridge books have been pouring off the presses for half a
century, ever since Harold Vanderbilt's celebrated cruise
inaugurated the contract era, and almost all of them have
proved unreadable. The typical book, on this side of the Atlantic
at any rate, is written by an expert whose vast knowledge of
technique is matched by a massive deficiency in writing skill.

Richard Crawford, the author of these lively tales, does not
fit the stereotype. He is an excellent writer, with a happy
facility for sketching the characters at a bridge table in a few
crisp lines. And although a good player, he is not an expert.
Technically-minded readers may occasionally find a flaw in
his analysis. But that is the fate of almost all bridge writers.
As a newspaper columnist I regularly receive letters from
readers challenging some statement I have made, and sometimes, unfortunately, they are right.

One can gather from these tales that the author's bridge life
has been spent in every variety of the game, ranging from the
Olympiads to the back-room table. While he does take some
interest in the esoteric systems that flourish nowadays in the
tournament world, his favorite hunting ground for his material
consists of the small clubs whose membership remains fairly
static year after year, and where characters are more significant
than conventions.

Almost all the characters are unidentifiable, but among the

5

exceptions, two stand out. One of them surfaces in the oft-told tale of the Bennett murder in Kansas City in 1929. There was a curious aftermath. Long after the attractive Mrs. Bennett had been acquitted of her husband's slaying by an impressionable jury, and a dazed insurance company had paid up on a life policy, Mrs. Bennett had trouble in obtaining bridge partners. Finally she found one who did not know her history. Apologizing for a considerable overbid, he put down his dummy, announcing, "Partner, you'll probably want to shoot me for this." And she fainted.

The only famous player to be treated at length in these pages is the late Adam Meredith, whose unique life style, that took him to small bridge clubs around the world as well as to a world title, was combined with a unique bidding style that baffled both his partners and his opponents. The author, while playing with Meredith, set out to match his partner in imagination. He reports a successful slam bid that few other players in the world would even consider.

Although the setting of these stories is international, it will probably be clear to the reader that the author is British, and the publisher American. To what extent Mr. Crawford has introduced fictional elements is for the reader to guess. But that does not really matter. What does matter is that they are fun to read.

Double Time

The man at the window turned his head towards the group huddled together in the middle of the room.

"Here they come," he said.

The group dispersed, and quickly took their places at the card tables; they picked up their cards and resumed the bidding and play which had been broken off some fifteen minutes previously when they had decided to hold their impromptu meeting. The man at the window remained where he was, but took a seat there and faced the door. He was the first to greet the newcomers.

"Hi, Peter. Hallo, Molly."

His greeting was returned affably by both the dashing young man with a handsome tan, a sporty blazer, a stylish cravat; and by his blonde wife, a fine-looking young woman whose teeth flashed in a ready smile, but whose eyes were as hard as diamonds. The pair looked around the room, saw that all the tables were in play, then went over to the window to engage the look-out man in cordial conversation.

Peter and Molly Delaporte had joined the small but exclusive Grandon Hills Bridge Club a few months previously. Peter let it be known that he was a "company director," but nobody had found out more than that. He wasn't seen around in the area very much, although he and his wife always managed to turn up for the weekly partnership session at the club. Rubber bridge could be played every afternoon of the week at the club, but the club's committee had decided some years previously to restrict partnership games to Saturdays only. The rest of the week, the members cut for partners. And because most members looked forward to playing with a partner of their choice, the normal rules regarding stakes had been tacitly relaxed, so that on Saturdays the stakes soared, competition was razor-keen, the atmosphere more than a little tense.

When Peter and Molly Delaporte joined the club, they played a few sessions of cut-in bridge and a few duplicates, but then they seemed to settle into a routine of playing on Saturdays only. And they won a great deal of money, so much in fact, as one member remarked thoughtfully to another, that even a company director might be envious.

The Delaportes played a strong game; their bidding, play and defence were well up to the standard of the club's best. Their luck in holding good cards was no better than average, but they had one particular weapon in their bidding armory which seemed to yield results quite out of the ordinary. As one member said to another, if it were not for that one feature of their game, they would be just another pair of bridge players.

On their very first visit, Peter had courteously informed his opponents: "We play the variable double, by the way."

"You play the what?"

"The variable double. It's simple enough. We prefer to come in with a take-out double on practically every type of overcall situation, rather than commit ourselves to a suit too early. The only exception is when the suit is self-sufficient."

"What's your range for this variable double?"

"There isn't one. That's why it's called variable. You'll find that our subsequent bidding will confirm whether the double was weak, medium or strong."

Neither of their opponents pressed for a more detailed

explanation, but in the session which followed, and the sessions on each succeeding Saturday, the variable double had been used with devastating effectiveness. This was one example:

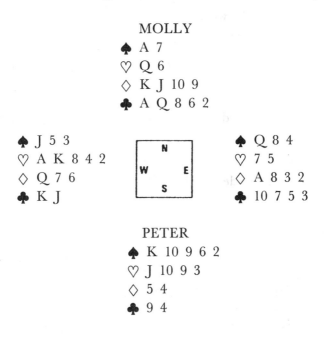

MOLLY
♠ A 7
♡ Q 6
◇ K J 10 9
♣ A Q 8 6 2

♠ J 5 3
♡ A K 8 4 2
◇ Q 7 6
♣ K J

♠ Q 8 4
♡ 7 5
◇ A 8 3 2
♣ 10 7 5 3

PETER
♠ K 10 9 6 2
♡ J 10 9 3
◇ 5 4
♣ 9 4

West dealt at game-all, and the bidding was:

W	N	E	S
1♡	dble	pass	pass(!)
pass			

Molly Delaporte led the Ace of Spades, continued with her other Spade, then ruffed the third round, after which she got off lead with the Queen of trumps. West struggled bravely, but had to go 2 down, losing 500.

Peter and Molly were all sympathy; they told West how cruel the distribution was, how lucky they had been to get their Spade ruff in the hand with the short trumps; how Peter had decided that he was so weak that he felt it would be less expensive to let West make a doubled 1 Heart contract, rather than get into deep water and finish up doubled himself.

It all sounded half-way plausible to East and West, who although grievously mortified at having lost 500 in a one-level contract, were made to feel that they were the victims of circumstances. But then, later during the same session, against different opponents, the variable double struck again:

PETER
♠ Q 8 7 4 3
♡ A 8 2
◇ A 2
♣ A 10 7

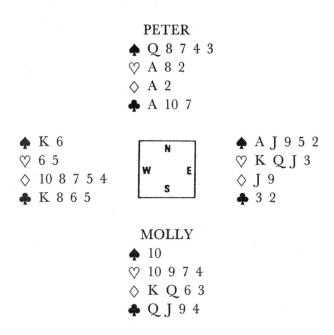

♠ K 6
♡ 6 5
◇ 10 8 7 5 4
♣ K 8 6 5

♠ A J 9 5 2
♡ K Q J 3
◇ J 9
♣ 3 2

MOLLY
♠ 10
♡ 10 9 7 4
◇ K Q 6 3
♣ Q J 9 4

East dealt, and the Delaportes were non-vulnerable, facing vulnerable opponents. The bidding went like this:

E	S	W	N
1♠	dble	pass	1 NT(!)
pass	2♣	pass	pass(!)
pass			

The King of Spades was led, followed by the 6, and Molly ruffed. She took two rounds of Diamonds, then led a small Diamond, ruffing with the 10 while East discarded a Heart honor. She then led the Ace and another trump, and when West won with his King, he returned a Heart. Molly took the Ace, and ruffed herself back into her hand by leading a Spade and using her last trump, the Queen, to take the trick. Then came the Queen of Diamonds, and when West had to follow suit, the eighth trick was in the bank.

"Two Clubs made," she announced coolly.

East and West were well aware that her double had been made on a very weak hand, and they were also aware of their astonishment at seeing dummy's strength: 14 points opposite a take-out double, yet he had stopped in 2 Clubs.

Peter knew the trend of their thoughts, and said casually to his wife: "I didn't see much point in going on. Once they forced out my Queen of Spades, the suit is dead in 3 NT, and I had the feeling that 5 Clubs was going to be hopeless. I just didn't have the shape for a high-level contract. Better to stop in something we could make."

Again, it sounded half-way plausible, and apart from a nameless nagging suspicion, East and West were content to let it drop and get on with the rubber.

But as the weeks went by, and as each week saw the Delaportes leaving the club with the equivalent of an executive's salary, the feelings began to harden. Small cliques whispered together. Then after a few more weeks, they coalesced into one

11

big clique. Something was wrong. The club members felt that they were being taken, although nobody could see how it was being done.

Then one day an unofficial meeting was called in great secrecy. After some guarded preliminary remarks, a more outspoken member cut impatiently through the verbiage and said:

"Now, look, we know why we're here. Peter and Molly Delaporte have some sort of agreement about this damn variable double of theirs. They always know when to stop, when to go on, when to turn the double into a penalty double, when to pass on a strong hand, when to bid up on a weak hand. Everybody in this room is convinced that they're doing something outside the laws and proprieties of the game. And nobody can pin it down. Right?"

He glared around, and the 30 or so members looked uneasily at him, but nobody challenged him. He continued.

"If we're right about this, it means there has to be a code, or a system of secret signals, or some illicit transfer of information. And if I'm right about that, the only way we can find what's going on is to keep watch. I take it nobody wants to alert them to the fact that they're under suspicion. Wouldn't do the club any good anyway, till we've got some proof. So we'll have to see they're watched at different times, by different people, and only for brief periods each time. Right?"

Again, general agreement. It was decided that three members, all men, would undertake this task for a month, and that at the end of that time there would be a further meeting to hear their report. When the meeting broke up, the three designated proctors got together. They discussed the most likely ways of conveying illegal information, and came to the conclusion that there were three main methods: by use of the voice, the eyes, or the fingers and hands. Each of the three men was assigned to make a special study of one of those features when watching the Delaportes at intervals during the next four Saturdays. They would then compare notes before the next scheduled meeting.

A little over a month later, those members who were in the know re-assembled. The three look-outs were summoned to deliver their reports, and each of them glumly conceded that there was nothing at all to report on. The man who had been allocated "voice" was the first to speak.

"I listened very carefully indeed, not just once or twice, but for a total of over six hours at various times this past month. There was no inflection; there was no detectable trace of variation of volume, tone or pitch in either of their voices; there was no clearing of the throat, or grunting, or little hesitant noises. Nothing at all, in fact. As far as my observation takes me, they're completely clean."

The "fingers and hands man" spoke next. "They did absolutely nothing with their fingers or hands that you or I wouldn't do. They sorted their cards in a completely normal way, and after that they held them in a completely normal way, and they sat absolutely still. No fidgeting or movement at all. As a matter of fact, if I'd been asked to report on members in general instead of just those two, I'd have had to say that they were the only ones incapable of sending signals by the use of their hands or other body movements."

The "eye specialist" then took the stage. "I sat behind one of them so that I could see the other one's face, and I switched around from week to week. From the time they picked up their cards until the time the hand was over, neither of them looked at the other at all. Their eyes were down on their cards the whole time."

The meeting sat silent, baffled and frustrated. For a long

moment, no one spoke. Then the club secretary said unhappily: "I guess this means that we have a straight choice. Either we get professional help from outside, or we just give up on the whole thing."

"What does professional help mean?" somebody asked.

"There's a man I used to know, in a city I won't name. He's had some experience with this sort of thing. Apparently it's fairly common where he comes from. We could get him into the club as a kind of under-cover member. Naturally, there would have to be a fee for his services . . ."

The proposal was voted on and carried, a phone call made, the fee agreed, and the man arrived. Three days later, on a Monday evening, he addressed a group of the assembled members.

"It didn't take me long," he started brusquely, "although I'm not surprised you took such a long time in finding out nothing. The average honest, ordinary, trusting player might not be able to reach my conclusion in years. As a matter of fact, it took me just one hour and twenty-five minutes. Your Mr. and Mrs. Delaporte took their places at the table at 8:15, and by 9:40 I had them nailed."

There was a chorus of exclamations and questions.

"It goes like this," said the expert. "They're both good enough players to know full well the kind of advantage their so-called variable double gives them when the partner of the doubler knows the strength of the doubling hand. So they rigged up a very simple little device to make sure that the necessary information reaches the partner without any danger that the average player would be able to intercept it. It's a little tough on them that I'm not the average player. Now, you want to know how they fixed things. Here's the scheme. Each two high-card points in the doubler's hand equals one second of time. When an opposing bid is made in front of the doubler, he's already made up his mind whether or not he's going to come in with a double. So the moment the bid is made, the doubler looks at his watch under the pretext of studying his cards. You may have noticed that both Mr. and Mrs. Delaporte wear their wristwatches so that the dial is on the inside of the wrist?"

No. Nobody had noticed.

"If Mr. Delaporte is going to double on a 12 point hand, he waits exactly 6 seconds after the opponent's bid, then says 'Double.' Mrs. Delaporte, with her eyes down apparently on her cards, has also been looking at her watch, and counting. After 6 seconds have gone by since the opponent made his bid, she hears her husband's double. She then knows quite a lot about his hand that she's not supposed to know. The pair of them might occasionally be one second or two points out, I guess, but certainly never more than two at the most. And best part of the time I'd say they'd be dead on."

"So that's how it's done," said the Grandon Hills secretary. "The next thing is, what can we do about it?"

"Nothing," said the expert. "You can't catch them in the act, because there's virtually no act. Over a long series of hands you could have them timed, then provide sworn testimony that the timed intervals coincided with the points. But even that wouldn't be conclusive. I doubt if it would stand up in court."

"But we gotta do something," said the secretary, peevishly. "I can't allow my members to be cheated out of their money week by week, and just sit by. What would you do if it was your problem?"

The expert shrugged. "Take a chance. See them privately. Tell them straight out that you're on to their little time-bomb. Tell them you have documentary evidence and statements by witnesses, whether you do or not. Say that, in order to preserve the reputation of the club, you are prepared to leave the police out of it, just so long as they send you their resignations in writing, for any reasons they care to dream up. It should work. I've known people like that; they suffer a lot of hurt pride when their precious little secret becomes public knowledge, and even though they might know that it's almost impossible for you to carry out the threat of calling in the law, the fact that they're being sneered at everywhere they go will be enough on its own to make them leave town in a hurry."

The secretary pondered this advice for a while, slowly nodding his head as he did so. Then suddenly his head jerked upright. "Hey!" he almost shouted. "You're leaving something out. How did you find out about the way they operate?"

"Oh, that," said the expert with an off-hand air. "I guess you lucky people down here take your sunshine for granted. Where I come from, the sun, together with its effects, is something of a phenomenon. So when I saw your clever little friends with their gorgeous sun-tans and their wristwatches on the wrong way round, I couldn't help noting that in each case there was a circle of quite pale skin on the outside of their wrists. They had obviously switched their watches round just for bridge once a week. Any other questions before I go?"

Much Too Vulnerable

Eventually, I suppose, most bridge writers feel impelled to say something about the Bennett murder. To someone who knows nothing of the emotional strains and psychological tensions of the game, this incident may seem just another sordid and rather pathetic tragedy, the kind of thing which rates half a column in local newspapers in every big city in the world at frequent intervals. But it was a green baize murder, and the bridge player—and certainly the bridge writer—sees in it the dimensions of a Greek tragedy. That is how it struck me when I first read about it, and that is how I see that doomed quartet around the table in Kansas City on a Sunday afternoon back in 1929. They appear to be playing parts already written for them, parts which are predestined to lead inexorably to the stark and bloody climax.

Mr. and Mrs. Bennett lived well, by the standards of that time and place. They enjoyed many of the good things of life, and they looked forward to their occasional game of bridge with their friends the Hoffmans. Mrs. Bennett, although not a good player, was a shade more capable than her husband, but she had developed the infuriating tendency of reminding him, loud and often, of his inadequacies.

Mr. and Mrs. Hoffman also enjoyed their bridge, but on that far-off Sunday afternoon the edge had gone from their pleasure. Acid and unmasked recrimination had passed between their opponents more than once; Mrs. Bennett had been increasingly sarcastic about her husband's bidding, play and defence, and he had been stung to retaliate. By the time the fatal hand was dealt, the atmosphere was strained and tense, the laughter had long died away, and brightness had gone from the room. In a dark and bitter mood, Mr. Bennett looked at the hand he had just dealt himself:

♠ K J 9 8 5
♡ K 7 6 2
♢ 8 5
♣ K 10

An ordinary hand; an unexciting hand; the kind of hand that could be forgotten completely within an hour of first looking at it. And a hand, surely, which qualifies as an automatic pass by the dealer. If Mr. Bennett had passed, he may have been alive today. But he made the very bad bid of 1 Spade, not knowing that in doing so he had set in motion the machinery of violent death.

Over Mr. Bennett's ill-conceived 1 Spade, Mr. Hoffman bid 2 Diamonds. Enter Mrs. Bennett, with a crude raise to 4 Spades.

If Mrs. Hoffman had been made of sterner stuff, she might have contested with 5 Diamonds, which cannot be badly mauled, but she passed, and the pace of events began to quicken. One tries to imagine Mr. Bennett's feelings on first seeing the dummy after Mr. Hoffman had led the Ace of Diamonds. Even a good player would have quailed inwardly, and Mr. Bennett was far from being a good player. Moreover, he must have been acutely conscious of the scorn and fury breathing at him from across the table.

After making his Ace of Diamonds, and studying the dummy, Mr. Hoffman switched to the Jack of Clubs, thereby offering

MRS. BENNETT
♠ A 10 6 3
♡ 10 8 5
♢ 4
♣ A 9 8 4 2

MR. HOFFMAN
♠ Q 7 2
♡ A J 3
♢ A Q 10 9 2
♣ J 6

MRS. HOFFMAN
♠ 4
♡ Q 9 4
♢ K J 7 6 3
♣ Q 7 5 3

MR. BENNETT
♠ K J 9 8 5
♡ K 7 6 2
♢ 8 5
♣ K 10

Mr. Bennett a longer lease of life. Many analysts have shown
that—as the cards actually lay—this switch enables the
contract to be made, and if Mr. Bennett had been capable of
lucid and detached analysis at that stricken table, he may have
preserved himself for who knows what future fate. The analysis
runs this way: West, at Trick 2, would surely seek to try to
cut down dummy's ruffing power by leading a trump. What
prevented him? Assume he was reluctant to lead away from
the guarded Queen. Assume, secondly, that the only way for
South to discard losing Hearts from his hand is by establishing
dummy's Clubs. Assume, finally, that the lead of the Jack by
West places the Queen with East.

The analysis continues: the play must be based on these

19

assumptions, so after taking the Club lead with the King, South plays the King of Spades and follows with the Jack. Whether or not West covers, declarer will shortly be in dummy after a trump lead, with all the adverse trumps drawn. Now the Ace of Clubs is played, followed by the 9, trapping East's Queen. Whether East chooses to cover or not, two Hearts are discarded from the South hand and the contract is brought home.

But under the stress of events, Mr. Bennett was incapable of this kind of rational analysis. He fumbled and blundered his way to inevitable defeat, stirring his wife to new excesses of scorn. When the last trick had been played, she exploded into a scathing and venomous tirade, humiliating him beyond endurance. He rose to his feet, and stretching across the table, slapped her hard.

Her last frail thread of sanity snapped. Boiling with anger, she rushed from the room, reappeared with a loaded revolver, and snarled inarticulately at him. Mr. Bennett suddenly realized she meant it, and in fear of his life made a dash for the nearest doorway, the one leading to the bathroom. But to the horror of the frightened Hoffmans, Mrs. Bennett fired. The shot rang deafeningly loud in the confined space. The fatal hand had reached its tragic climax. One down. And that one was Mr. Bennett.

Cyclone

On those mercifully rare occasions when a severe storm hits the Bahamas, it arrives between July and October. But in 1967 a one-man storm arrived about four months early, and although he stayed only a few weeks, the havoc he caused is still vividly remembered.

"Keep young and beautiful
If you want to be loved."

While Adam Meredith was in Nassau, he sang that little couplet incessantly from morning to night, and I never hear it these days without immediately thinking of that cyclonic period when he showed us a range and depth of individuality which is rare enough in any pursuit, but rarer still at the bridge table.

None of us who had the privilege of sitting at the table with him are likely to forget him in a hurry. Tall and rangy, with a great mane of wavy hair, penetrating blue eyes, and an unforced charm of manner, he proved to be not simply a law unto himself, but a whole system of laws which lay outside normal rationale. His bridge, like his life, was full of unpredictable twists and turns, and the combination of brilliance and audacity, which was his hallmark, had the effect of mesmerizing his opponents.

Whether you were his partner or his opponent, there was always this slightly frightening but exhilarating feeling of driving at blinding speed through thick fog. His intensely

21

unconventional and intuitive bidding kept you poised on the threshold of dramatic revelation; his genius in the play of the cards kept you wondering how he made so many bricks with such little straw.

By nature—and I suspect by choice—Meredith was a rubber bridge player, though he had a fine tournament record. He represented Britain in the memorable World Championship final of 1955, having been selected as much for his nuisance value to the enemy as anything else. He justified his inclusion on those grounds, quite apart from his fine technique. Here is one hand from that match. West was the dealer at game-all:

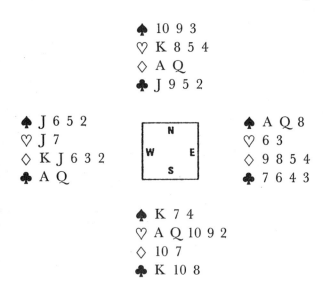

♠ 10 9 3
♡ K 8 5 4
◇ A Q
♣ J 9 5 2

♠ J 6 5 2
♡ J 7
◇ K J 6 3 2
♣ A Q

♠ A Q 8
♡ 6 3
◇ 9 8 5 4
♣ 7 6 4 3

♠ K 7 4
♡ A Q 10 9 2
◇ 10 7
♣ K 10 8

In one room, after bidding which went:

W	N	E	S
1◇	pass	2◇	2♡
pass	4♡		all pass

Terence Reese, South, got his Clubs going early, and made his contract, losing only 2 Clubs and a Spade, when West failed to shift to Spades in time. 620 to Britain.

At the other table, Meredith sat West. More than most players in those days, he exploited the pre-emptive value of the Spade suit, coming in with a Spade bid whenever his cards even remotely justified it. On this occasion he saw no objection to J 6 5 2 as a biddable suit, and the brief auction went:

W	N	E	S
1 ♠	pass	2 ♠	all pass

He was able to make his contract by careful play, but the main ingredient in this big swing to Britain was the tactical advantage which Meredith created by his Spade opening.

It was at the rubber table, however, that the full flavor of Meredith's surrealist approach to the game could be appreciated. I remember with pain the very first hand we played as partners. I remember with deep satisfaction and pleasure some of the subsequent ones. And I remember with utter astonishment some of his more exotic forays. That first hand was grim enough to turn our half of the table into a disaster area, but it taught me a useful lesson. After gravely tutoring me in the species of Acol which he liked to play, Meredith dealt and opened 1 Spade (what else!). I held:

> ♠ K Q
> ♡ A J 3 2
> ◇ Q J 5
> ♣ Q 4 3 2

After a pass on my right, I made what I thought was the

textbook Acol response of 3 NT. But apparently neither my left-hand opponent nor my illustrious partner had read that chapter of the textbook, because LHO doubled, all passed, and Meredith's hand was displayed as dummy. Frowning at me, he put down:

♠ 5 3 2
♡ 10 8 5 4
♢ 7 6 2
♣ K 9 8

I was prepared to cope with a ragged 11 points, but a balanced 3 . . . Amid a strained silence I limped away from the wreckage. 1,300 down. LHO had held a good 7-card Spade suit and two Aces, and had decided that Meredith or no Meredith, we were not going to make 9 tricks. How right he was. And for a few seconds I had thought seriously of re-doubling!

Meredith apologized handsomely, but immediately after-wards, shaking his great leonine head solemnly, stressed the folly of accepting as literal truth any bid of his. Shortly after that, when I was kibitzing the same table, I had the visible proof of that statement. Already in that rubber, Meredith had been busy. There were a number of little part-scores snatched against the odds, undoubled sacrifices in the enemy's own suit, and opposition contracts mysteriously defeated by uncanny defence. His opponents were becoming rattled.

He then took advantage of their state of mind by opening 3 Spades when he had quite a strong hand. The take-out double was left in for penalties. This would have worked very profitably two hands previously, but the axe came down too late, and the overtricks rolled in. The enemy were by now more than rattled; they were becoming unhinged, and were psychologically ripe for the incredible coup which followed:

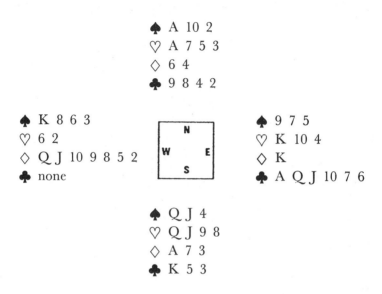

```
                    ♠ A 10 2
                    ♡ A 7 5 3
                    ◇ 6 4
                    ♣ 9 8 4 2

♠ K 8 6 3                           ♠ 9 7 5
♡ 6 2              N                 ♡ K 10 4
◇ Q J 10 9 8 5 2  W   E             ◇ K
♣ none                S             ♣ A Q J 10 7 6

                    ♠ Q J 4
                    ♡ Q J 9 8
                    ◇ A 7 3
                    ♣ K 5 3
```

Sitting South, vulnerable against non-vulnerable opponents, Meredith, as dealer, opened 3 Clubs! To this day I don't know what went through his mind; perhaps he didn't know his own reasons for that extraordinary stroke. But he was keenly sensitive to the psychological atmosphere, and maybe he felt that no matter what he did, he would be able to control the situation.

West was bemused enough to pass. North passed, and East doubled. Meredith made a serene pass, and even though it was understood that the double was for penalties, West was having none of that, and smartly removed to 3 Diamonds. When this was passed round to Meredith, he had the sheer nerve to double. After two more passes, East, in frustration, rage and bewilderment, took it out to 3 NT, which also got doubled. Poor West, with whom we must surely sympathize, reverted to 4 Diamonds. Again Meredith doubled implacably, and the contract duly bit the dust.

For cold daring, for deliberate psychological pressure amounting almost to torture, for "table presence" at its most intense, that hand is the supreme example in all my experience.

It takes time to adjust to the Meredith approach to bridge, but once I had been able to do so to some extent I enjoyed being his partner, and even found that on occasions I was able to tune in to his zany wavelengths with varying degrees of accuracy. During an exciting high-stake game towards the end of his stay in Nassau, I found myself with the following hand in the South position:

♠ K 2
♡ A 8 3 2
♢ J 10
♣ K Q 9 8 7

With Meredith North, East dealt at game-all. The bidding started:

E	S	W	N
1 ♡	2 ♣	2 ♠	3 NT

With almost any partner, and on 99 out of 100 occasions, I should have passed without hesitation. But this was the 100th occasion, and my partner was one in a million. My imagination waited to catch some extra-sensory vibrations which would enable me to make contact with his normally unfathomable thought-processes. The answer came in a blinding flash of revelation. Feeling more than a little heady, I bid 6 Diamonds! Never before and never since could I have done such a thing.

But everybody passed, West led a trump, and as dummy went down I had the gratifying spectacle of Adam Meredith's head nodding calmly in approval. The full hand was:

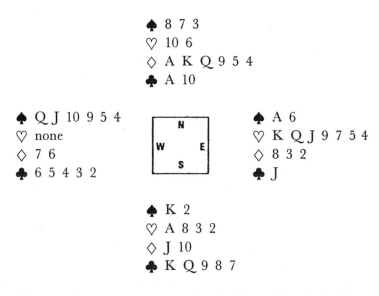

```
                    ♠ 8 7 3
                    ♡ 10 6
                    ◇ A K Q 9 5 4
                    ♣ A 10

♠ Q J 10 9 5 4              ♠ A 6
♡ none          N          ♡ K Q J 9 7 5 4
◇ 7 6        W     E        ◇ 8 3 2
♣ 6 5 4 3 2     S          ♣ J

                    ♠ K 2
                    ♡ A 8 3 2
                    ◇ J 10
                    ♣ K Q 9 8 7
```

After drawing trumps, I went for the Clubs. The Jack fell on the first round, so there was no problem. Sweating a little, I claimed my 12 tricks, and waited to be congratulated on what I regarded as an inspired inferential bid.

The congratulations came later; I first had to listen to a stern lecture from my partner on the play of the hand. He showed me that I should draw trumps, play Clubs, discarding dummy's Spades, ruff myself back into dummy with a Spade, and come down to:

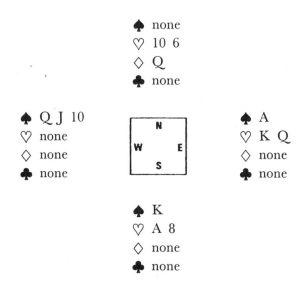

The Queen of Diamonds would then squeeze East, and I could discard according to whichever form of suicide East chose to commit.

Meredith then bestowed a few words of praise for my leap to 6 Diamonds, which was probably routine to him, then continued to rebuke me for failing to execute the squeeze for the overtrick. It was not the monetary value of the extra trick which mattered to him, but I had somehow violated the artistic integrity of the partnership by so crudely going for my 12 tricks.

Meredith is dead now, but in the minds of all who met him, he will surely keep young and beautiful. His dashing style and his open nature will surely see to that. And, in memory, he will be loved.

The Ten-Minute Genius

Do you really believe that truth is stranger than fiction? Honestly, now, do you? Most people don't. Most people, while paying lip-service to that venerable adage, privately believe that the inventiveness of a writer can easily outshine reality, and that events lying far beyond the realm of prosaic fact can be conjured up by an effort of the imagination.

My own convictions put me solidly in the opposite camp. I'm on the side of the adage, and I should like to put in evidence a true story, which has been fully authenticated by eye-witnesses, and which by comparison makes any similar fictional account seem like a mere shadow.

We go back to 1933. Contract Bridge, although relatively in its infancy, was nevertheless sweeping the United States like a forest fire. Duplicate was already firmly entrenched, and most states had their own State Championship. The numbers of players travelling beyond their own state lines to play in these championships mounted every month. Among them was Norman Bonney, a resident of Boston, who in that year made a trip to New Hampshire especially to take part in the New Hampshire Championship.

Mr. Bonney suffered from a weak heart, and although it curtailed some of his activities, he did not allow it to interfere with his bridge. The first afternoon of play was devoted to a pairs event, during which Mr. Bonney sat East on the following deal:

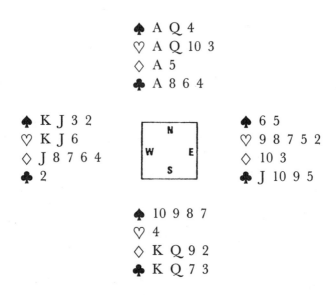

♠ A Q 4
♥ A Q 10 3
♦ A 5
♣ A 8 6 4

♠ K J 3 2
♥ K J 6
♦ J 8 7 6 4
♣ 2

♠ 6 5
♥ 9 8 7 5 2
♦ 10 3
♣ J 10 9 5

♠ 10 9 8 7
♥ 4
♦ K Q 9 2
♣ K Q 7 3

North and South, who must have been the original Odd Couple, somehow blundered into the farcical contract of 7 No Trump. West led the 2 of Spades, and within a few minutes it was all over. 2 down. After some desultory remarks from South on the impossibility of doing any better, there was a brief discussion among the four at the table. They turned their cards face upward while they all tried to figure out whether there was any chance at all. The major suit honors were well placed, it was true, but the distribution of the adverse minor suit holdings was such that it seemed to all of them that 2 down was indeed a richly deserved fate for such an over-ambitious contract.

Before the cards were finally put back in the board, South turned to Mr. Bonney and asked plaintively, "There really isn't any way I can make 7, is there?"

Bonney, who did not see himself as an expert analyst, took one last long look at the deal and slowly shook his head.

"If there is, I can't see it," he answered. And they turned their attention to the next board.

The pairs event in which they were playing was divided into two halves, the second half taking place later in the evening. When Mr. Bonney arrived in the foyer of the hotel, he was rather early for the evening session, so he got into conversation with W. Mark Noble, a well-known player of that time and place. Mr. Noble was a cripple who had lost the use of his legs and was confined to a wheelchair.

The hotel had two floors only, and did not boast an elevator, so the question arose of getting Mr. Noble upstairs into the card room. By now there was a steady stream of players passing through on their way to the tournament, and it was not difficult for Mr. Bonney to persuade one of them to help him with Mr. Noble. They hoisted him bodily from his wheelchair and lifted him up the stairs and along the corridor to the card room. Then they placed him at one of the tables while they awaited the arrival of his wheelchair. But immediately after Mr. Noble had been settled, Mr. Bonney's heart, overstrained by this unaccustomed exertion, went on strike. He passed out.

He was soon surrounded by a circle of anxious duplicate players who fanned him, loosened his collar, poured water on his brow, and performed other useful acts inspired not only by fellow-feeling, but also by the knowledge that a death in the room would leave the tournament one short, a calamitous contingency.

Suddenly, without warning, Mr. Bonney leapt to his feet, white-faced and trembling. The crowd drew back in alarm.

"My God!" shouted Mr. Bonney in a hoarse voice.

Nobody spoke. They felt sure that they were about to witness his last moment, and his imminent collapse onto the floor seemed only a few seconds away. But Norman Bonney had other plans, as they soon found out.

"I've got it," he said, and staggered to one of the card tables, where he took a deck of cards, and with the others trailing uncertainly after him, he proceeded to reconstruct the 7 NT deal with every card in every hand perfectly positioned. Then he turned to the assembled throng and said:

"I can make 7 No Trump on this hand, and here's how it's done."

He worked swiftly and confidently, showing the hushed circle of spectators one of the most fantastic squeeze positions ever brought to light. In his book, "Endplays," George Coffin, the eminent authority on squeezes, describes this incident, which he calls the New Hampshire Miracle; Coffin gives the end-position the technical title of Triple-Double Automatic Repeating Squeeze. In the whole museum of bridge wonders, it might easily be the only one of its kind. But a bigger wonder lay behind it.

Norman Bonney was a useful player but no expert; he was interested enough in the theory of the game to have his own ideas on the subject, but he readily disclaimed any pretensions to the title of analyst. Think of some member of your club who does quite well at the game most of the time, and you've thought of Mr. Bonney. And yet this whole esoteric package had been delivered to him via his unconscious mind while he lay on the floor in a dead faint.

Now he turned over the cards in each hand trick by trick as he explained to his audience how the extraordinary 6-card ending was reached.

"South lets the opening lead run to his own hand. Then he finesses dummy's Queen of Spades and cashes the Ace. Next come the Ace and Queen of Clubs, followed by the Ace and

His audience, still full of anxiety about a different kind of heart trick, persuaded him to sit and relax for a while, and as Mr. Bonney's strength returned, they left him to take their places at the tables, and play began.

Norman Bonney didn't win. He didn't win all that many tournaments after he rose to the height Eastern Pair Champion in 1931, and didn't expect to. But the incident in which he had been the central figure started him off on a quest for unusual end-positions so that he later became a well-known collector of such curiosities. But until the day of his death he was unable to explain how it was that his dormant faculties had precision-engineered such an intricate and meticulous solution to a problem which would confound most of the world's experts. Nor was he able to repeat such a feat, waking or sleeping, playing or fainting.

The rare and remarkable freak of genius which had possessed him just that once was never to return.

Queen of Diamonds. That leaves the 6 cards in each ha
like this:"

Mr. Bonney pointed a shaking finger at the layout of t
end game:

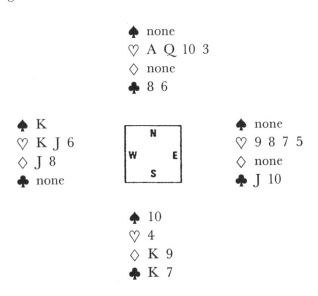

♠ none
♡ A Q 10 3
♢ none
♣ 8 6

♠ K
♡ K J 6
♢ J 8
♣ none

♠ none
♡ 9 8 7 5
♢ none
♣ J 10

♠ 10
♡ 4
♢ K 9
♣ K 7

"Now," Mr. Bonney went on, "South plays his two King
And in the manner of a professor stunned and enraptured
the beauty of his own discovery, he added: "In fact, it does
matter in which order he cashes them; the effect is the sar
West must hang on to a Diamond, East must keep a Club.
West is also obliged to keep his King of Spades, he m
throw a Heart.

"If either or both the opponents refuse to let go a Hea
they will be subjected to a repeating squeeze in the ot
suits. If they do throw Hearts, South can take the He
finesse, then by straight leads, pick up the last four He
tricks."

A Personal Everest

After the dust has settled at the conclusion of a big tournament or an international championship, some scribe is likely to seize on a hand which seems to contain outstanding interest or drama, and place it in nomination for the title of Hand of the Week. A bridge publication I used to subscribe to was in the habit of featuring the Hand of the Month. For all I know, somebody might also have chosen a particular arrangement of 52 cards as Hand of the Year.

Indulge me while I go even further. The true tale I am about to unfold must rank as my own Hand of a Lifetime. Among all the many thousands of hands which have amused me or amazed me, baffled me or buffetted me, this one stands out with such pre-eminence that it occupies, for me, a very special place. You could call it a personal Everest.

Towards the end of a very long and unusually tough and adventurous session of rubber bridge, the four of us were all slightly under the influence. Not of alcohol, however, but of that headiness which comes from sustained contact with the odd, the improbable and the hazardous. We were ripe for the extraordinary sequence of events which sprang from the cards dealt by North, my partner, at a time when we were vulnerable and East-West had not scored. My hand was:

♠ none
♡ A 10 7 5
♢ J 9 5 3
♣ K Q J 9 2

Come with me now through time and space, and sit beside me as the auction gets under way.

North examines his cards briefly, then passes. East makes his usual non-committal pass. This has given me a few seconds in which to decide that at unfavorable vulnerability, in the company of super-optimists, egomaniacs and predators, an opening bid is not likely to take our side very far along the paths of glory. I pass.

Not the least strange of all the strange features of this deal is that it might have been thrown in. This particular West, however, is not the kind of player who is easily able to pass. He says 1 Club.

It is not necessary for my partner to ask East about the meaning of West's bid. We know they are not playing one of the 1 Club systems; West is presumed to have either a natural Club hand, a hand containing equal Clubs and Spades, or possibly the equivalent of a weak No Trump. North deliberates for a while, then produces a double. East says 1 Heart, and now it's my turn.

When I tell you that I bid a modest 2 Diamonds, I do so without shame. In the present company I have learned the hard way that a conservative view at any time is a necessary item in my survival kit. We are playing for formidable stakes, and the entire table is somewhat trigger-happy. Moreover, partner is marked with a Spade suit, which doesn't overwhelm me with joy.

West now passes, and North raises me to 3 Diamonds. This comes as no surprise, but is hardly exhilarating. East passes, and I have to decide whether to leave things well alone or to put a tentative foot forward in some direction or other. I try to form a picture of North's hand: a Spade-Diamond two-suiter, no doubt; at least one Diamond honor, but a meagre point count. We can probably make 3 Diamonds on a cross-ruff, I tell myself, and if partner has exactly the right cards we can make one or two more. (You will appreciate the irony of the fact that – for the second time – ignominy stood waiting in the wings.)

In the end I convince myself that if I now bid 3 Hearts, partner will know that it's control-showing, and that I'm looking for extra prospects of game in Diamonds. If this doesn't excite him, I say to myself, he'll bail out in 4 Diamonds, and that will be quite high enough for me. So I bid 3 Hearts.

After another pass from West, North now says 3 Spades. And just as the misgivings begin to crowd into my mind, East comes to life again and says 4 Clubs. I am elated. The struggle is over. I can forget my mental exercises with the distributional scene, and grab the certain penalty which dear old reckless East has just offered us. I double.

West, trying to look and sound like a man completely unconcerned, passes, but North now goes into a prolonged trance. At one point he raises his head long enough to ask for a review of the bidding, then sinks back into his slumberous posture. Suddenly, his head snaps upright, and fixing me with an alarmingly wild stare, he says 4 Hearts.

I really don't know what to make of this. In fact, the whole performance is starting to get to me. Here is a man – and quite a shrewd bidder most of the time – who passes as dealer and who hears his partner pass. OK, so he contests the fourth-in-hand opener with a light distributional double. He likes my Diamond response, he raises the Diamonds, he bids Spades, and now he takes out my punitive and profitable double of 4 Clubs in order to bid East's suit. What's going on?

A new thought strikes me. Was East fooling around when he first bid 1 Heart? Knowing this East, it is not an impossible contingency. Can my partner be 5–4–4–0? I go back carefully over the bidding. No, he can't. So he's either showing me a Heart void, which seems equally improbable, or more likely he's got the King of Hearts and is encouraging me to look for a slam.

Despite my desperate desire to anchor myself to prudence and practicality, I seem to catch the far-off sound of bugles and kettle-drums. I now bid 4 Spades.

This turns out to be neither prudent nor practical. It has a galvanic and horrifying effect on North. After a calm pass by West, my partner takes on a frightening aspect. He hoists himself suddenly to his full height in his chair; he leans far forward; he closes his eyes; one hand clutches his cards close to his chest while the other, with fingers stiff and extended, hovers in the air over the middle of the table. He remains like this for a full 30 seconds while I start anxiously to frame my excuses. How can he possibly think that I'm supporting Spades, runs my prepared speech, when I've already ignored several previous opportunities to do so. And what's more – but North theatrically interrupts my interior monologue. Still holding his Grand Guignol pose, but with eyes bulging open and cheeks distended, he is ready for utterance.

He bellows out: "Seven Diamonds!"

East passes. With sinking heart I pass. West announces a sharp and chilling double. All pass. The thunder of the auction rolls away from the table, leaving me feeling wretched, penitent, and angry with myself for allowing events to take hold of me and carry me along so incontinently to this point of no return.

The whole auction, which must have taken close to 15 minutes, has been:

N	E	S	W
pass	pass	pass	1 ♣
dble	1 ♡	2 ◇	pass
3 ◇	pass	3 ♡	pass
3 ♠	4 ♣	dble	pass
4 ♡	pass	4 ♠	pass
7 ◇	pass	pass	dble
pass	pass	pass	

West considers his opening lead for a long time, while my impatience mounts. What on earth am I going to see in dummy? Finally, West places the Queen of Hearts on the table, and North, who appears to be back to normal, puts down his cards with a defiant scowl. And this is what I see:

♠ J 10 9 8 6
♡ K 3
◇ A Q 8 6 4 2
♣ none

And, as a reminder, this is my hand:

♠ none
♡ A 10 7 5
◇ J 9 5 3
♣ K Q J 9 2

So there I was. North and I, two hardened performers who had both passed originally, now found ourselves in a doubled vulnerable grand slam, not goaded there by sacrificial necessity, but freely bid. I stared gloomily at dummy.

The panic which had gripped me after West's double started to abate. Clearly, I was going to make a lot of tricks. But all

13? I needed to get out of my pessimistic mood, and concentrate on forming some kind of plan. I settled down to think.

I didn't apologize to the rest of the table as the minutes ticked by. Truculence had set in. Let 'em suffer, I thought, and that included my impulsive partner.

West had bid 1 Club. East had raised the Clubs at a dangerously high level. I decided to make an *a priori* assumption that the suit was 4–4. If this were so, West could have no more than four Spades, since he would have bid them rather than Clubs if he had 5. So give East five Hearts for his 1 Heart response, add four Clubs and four Spades, and that meant a void in Diamonds.

Now what about the key honor cards? I had to assume that West held the King of Diamonds and the Ace of Clubs, otherwise all was lost anyway. What about the Jack of Hearts? If West held the Queen and Jack, he would have never taken as long as he did over finding an opening lead. The mists started to clear slowly.

Still ignoring all the fidgeting going on around me, I continued to put up little diagrams on my mental blackboard. It was the likely 3–0 trump split that caused me to erase each one of them. I got as far as this for example, trick by trick:

1. Win with dummy's King of Hearts.
2. Ruff a Spade.
3. Play the Jack of Diamonds. Holding K 10 7 West would cover.
4. Return to hand via the Ace of Hearts.
5. Lead the King of Clubs, ruffing West's Ace.
6. Ruff another Spade.
7. Play the Queen of Clubs.
8. Play the Jack of Clubs.
9. Ruff a Club.

Straining hard, I visualized the end-position like this, with the lead in dummy:

♠ J
♡ none
◇ Q 8 6
♣ none

♠ none
♡ 10 7
◇ 9
♣ 2

Now, I thought, if I ruff the Jack of Spades with my last trump then lead a Heart, am I home? Only if the trumps are 2–1, I realized sadly, because otherwise I'd have to lose the last trick to West's 10 of trumps. Was there any way I could relieve West of one of his trumps before I reached that point?

Then it hit me. I brightened, and East and West glared at me suspiciously. I won the Heart lead with the King, but then immediately led the small Heart, and with trembling fingers inserted the 10. It held. Now the King of Clubs, at which West looked askance. He shrugged, and played the Ace. As I ruffed in dummy, I fought down my rising jubilation. Two more crests to climb.

A small Spade followed from dummy, East hopefully crunching in with the Ace. I ruffed, then tried my little inspiration. I played the Ace of Hearts.

I don't think that West, bless his greedy soul, even looked at that as a form of temptation. He was just not the kind of player who would be capable of shrinking from the chance to trump declarer's Ace in a grand slam. Not this implacable West. No, sir. He ruffed. Dummy over-ruffed. One more crest before the peak.

Back to hand with another Spade ruff, I played the Queen and Jack of Clubs, discarding Spades from dummy. Then came a Heart ruff and yet another Spade ruff. I was down to the Jack of Diamonds and two small Clubs, while dummy had A Q 6 of trumps.

"This is it," I said to North, who was showing signs of wear and tear. At last, I took the trump finesse, which worked, and I flopped back in my chair, exhausted, elated, and beyond any sensation except the wine-sweet and pulsating triumph which sang in my veins.

Even when North started to castigate me on my bidding, and later when East and West sourly reminded me that everything had been in my favor, it quite failed to diminish that intoxicating realization that I had assailed the summit, had stood there in awe, and had returned to the foothills unscathed.

Here is the full deal:

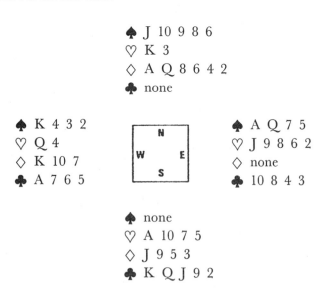

Later, from the safety of the foothills, I cast a reflective glance at the route to the summit. West did indeed make life easier for me by ruffing my Ace of Hearts, but had he refused to ruff, I still had a path to take. I could have thrown a Spade from dummy, then subsequently take two finesses through West. First I should lead the Jack of Diamonds, which would be covered by the King and Ace. Then after ruffing a Spade with the 9, I could lead my 5 of trumps through West's 10 and 7, with dummy holding the Q 8, and others.

But when you are clinging to the slopes, faced with a 10,000-foot drop, you can be forgiven for failing to notice that the man who is aiming blows at your lifeline has already hacked halfway through his own!

Alfred

Bridge players come in different shapes, sizes, nationalities and abilities. They can also be classified in terms of their liking for the game, ranging from the player who doesn't care much whether he plays or not, at one end of the scale, to the irreclaimable addict at the other. For anyone who chose to classify players in that way, Alfred Mayhill would present a problem. Probably the only satisfactory solution would be to add a new category at the far end of the scale, and let Alfred occupy it all by himself.

Alfred lived only for bridge. He was a bachelor, of course, as no woman could put up for long with an absentee husband whose mistress was a table and 52 cards. I knew him years ago, in the town where I used to live, and I sometimes wondered what he would have done with his life if there were no such game as bridge. I suppose he would have had to invent it himself. All his conversation was about the game, and seemingly all his inner thoughts too.

At the time I knew him, he kept a little hardware store, but he usually kept it closed, since he was either in the local bridge club, or else out of town at some tournament. He really couldn't be bothered all that much about making a living, because it deprived him of valuable time which could be better spent at the bridge table.

The inevitable result, of course, was that his customers drifted away, discouraged by the ever-closed door. So he hired a bright young man to look after the business while he attended to more important matters. But the young man proved to be a shade too bright, and one day he disappeared, taking with him all the cash he could lay his hands on, plus quite a bit of the stock as well.

Alfred and I belonged to the same club, and I can remember the time we were sitting enjoying a session of rubber bridge early one afternoon. It was a pleasant but uneventful session, until the tranquility of the room was ruffled by the entry of a grim and purposeful man whom none of us had seen before. He came in just as a hand had been dealt, and as we sorted our cards, he coughed in a respectful way, and said:

"Any of you gentlemen know a Mr. Alfred Mayhill?"

"I've known him for some time," said Alfred cheerfully. He had that corny sort of humor at times. Then he said more seriously, "As a matter of fact, that's me."

"I'm Detective-Sergeant Evans. May I have a word with you in private, sir?"

"Can it wait for about ten minutes?" asked Alfred. He was holding a most attractive assortment of cards, and unless it were a matter of life and death, he couldn't see how any emergency could take priority. And even in a matter of life and death, Alfred was not at all sure that the cards ought to be kept waiting.

The officer appeared to be a bit miffed.

"Couldn't you make that five minutes, sir?" he asked rather irritably. "I do have a very heavy schedule."

Alfred turned to the rest of us. "Let's bid it first," he proposed, "then I'll see what this is all about. When I get back, we'll play the hand. OK?"

Nobody argued, so the bidding began. Here is the hand, on which Alfred sat South, while I occupied the West seat.

                    ♠ J 8 4
                    ♡ K 5 4 3
                    ◇ Q 10 2
                    ♣ 9 8 6

♠ Q   ♠ A 9 3
♡ A Q J 9 8 7 6   N   ♡ 10 2
◇ 5 4 3   W   E   ◇ J
♣ 10 7   S   ♣ K Q J 5 4 3 2

                    ♠ K 10 7 6 5 2
                    ♡ none
                    ◇ A K 9 8 7 6
                    ♣ A

My partner dealt, and the bidding was something like this:

E	S	W	N
1 ♣	dble	1 ♡	pass
2 ♣	3 ◇	3 ♡	pass
pass	3 ♠	4 ♣	pass
pass	4 ♠	pass	5 ◇
pass	6 ◇		all pass

When the bidding was over, Alfred took a last look at his
hand, then left the room with Evans. They were away about
fifteen minutes. We found afterwards that it was a routine
enquiry about the absconding young man. When Alfred came
bustling back into the room, he picked up his cards, and said
to me briskly, "Your lead against 6 Diamonds."

I led the 10 of Clubs, taken by the Ace. Alfred played a
low trump to dummy's Queen, staring intently at East's Jack.

Then he led the Jack of Spades from dummy. When East played a small Spade, Alfred immediately produced his King, which dropped my Queen. Then came the Ace of trumps and a low trump to dummy's 10. Now a Spade lead from dummy, and it was all over.

"Six Diamonds bid and made," announced Alfred, with his cherubic smile.

The rest of us were still a bit subdued from the recent visit of the law, but Alfred chattered away about his slam as if nothing else of any importance had taken place during the whole of that day. And to him, it hadn't.

A few weeks after that, I left the town, and it was nearly nine years before I paid a return visit. I went along to the bridge club, and there was Alfred, cheerful as ever. As soon as I saw him, I thought of the young man who had run off with the money. Had the police caught up with him? Had the money and stock been restored? I reminded Alfred that the affair had taken place just before I had left town, and that in fact I had been in the very room we were in at that moment when the detective had come in to make enquiries.

"Ah, yes," said Alfred, his eyes lighting up, "I remember that day all right; I was in 6 Diamonds. Most interesting hand. If I pull three rounds of trumps I can never—."

"Alfred," I cut in, "what happened to that young man? Did he go to jail?"

"Hanged if I can remember now," said Alfred off-handedly. "Never had much of a head for trifles. It was such a long time ago. But I can tell you one thing: when I play a Spade straight away when I'm in dummy I can never get home if the Ace goes up and your Queen drops. I'll get another Spade led, and you'll trump the second round, won't you, old scout?"

The old scout dumbly nodded assent. If Alfred said that nine years before, I would have ruffed a Spade, I was prepared to admit that I would. I made one last effort.

"What about your money? Did the police get it back?"

Alfred opened his mouth to answer, but at that same moment there came a cry of "Table!" From then on, it was bridge all the way, and I never did find out.

The Golden Fleece

You are in the United States on a business trip, and having completed most of what you set out to do, you are sitting in a train, bound for New Orleans, where you will be catching your flight for home. Sitting facing you is a serious-looking young man, engrossed in a book. In the other corner is an older man who is gazing thoughtfully out of the window. You exchange a few words with both of them, and find them courteous and friendly.

Presently, another man makes his way along the corridor and puts his head in, smiles, and says, "Anyone here interested in a few rubbers of bridge?"

Eagerly you nod your head. Your two companions also seem to find the idea a welcome one, because they both nod their heads, and the younger man puts his book away. The newcomer produces two decks of cards, the modest stakes suggested seem agreeable to all, the cut for partners is made, and the game begins.

The time passes very pleasantly. It turns out that all your companions are good players, and you find the bidding and play sharp enough for your taste. They are good company, too, and you are enjoying yourself so much that it comes as a stab of regret when one of them announces that they had better regard the next hand as the last one as there is only another ten minutes before the train reaches New Orleans.

The man who originally suggested the game also thinks so.

He has just come back from the bathroom, and on hearing that this must be the last hand, he registers obvious disappointment. It is his turn to deal, and as he deals the cards, you notice nothing out of the ordinary. But the auction which then follows is far from ordinary. Your hand is:

♠ none
♡ K J 9 7 5 3 2
◇ Q J 10
♣ Q J 4

The dealer, whom you know only as Hal, sits on your right. As you look at your cards, it occurs to you that if he passes, you have a fairly orthodox opening of 3 Hearts. It is game-all, and such a bid might prevent them finding a high Spade contract. While you are musing along those lines, you are suddenly astonished to hear Hal open the bidding with 1 Heart.

This is much to your liking, of course, but it also rules out any possibility of taking any action yourself. You pass, awaiting events. You don't have long to wait. Your left-hand opponent says 2 Diamonds. Now your partner comes to life with 2 Spades. He would, you tell yourself.

But now Hal says 3 Hearts without any hesitation whatever. You hesitate for even less time in making your double. It'll be sweet to bow out of the game with a nice juicy penalty, you say to yourself. But the auction is not yet over. Your left-hand opponent, looking worried, thinks for a while, then passes. Then partner, curse his foolish headstrong nature, persists with 3 Spades, and the visions of that nice juicy penalty rapidly fade. Looks like trouble ahead. And then, wonder of wonders, Hal bids 4 Hearts!

You have been brought up to regard inflections in tone during the auction as not only unsporting, but downright unethical, but all that training is laid aside as you fill your lungs for the double of a lifetime. Your one thought is to drive it into the head of your wayward partner that he mustn't even consider doing any further bidding in case he deprives the two of you of your rich and rightful heritage. Your double can be heard half-way down the length of the train.

There is no more bidding, but Hal apparently has taken exception to the way you produced that double. His expression is severe, his tone glacial. "So you think you can beat my contract," he observes. "I happen to think I can make it. Want to have a side-bet on it?"

You glance again at your cards. At least 3—quite possibly 4 —trump tricks, Spades to make when partner gets in, stoppers in both the other suits. It's a bonanza.

"Whatever you like," you say crisply. You take a look in your wallet, and can count $600. What a pity. You wish it were $6,000. However, you take out the $600, which Hal immediately matches with $600 of his own, and the money is put into the custody of your partner. The bet is a simple one: if he makes his contract, Hal pockets the money; if he fails, even by one trick, it's all yours. You never felt more confident in your whole life.

"Your lead," says Hal.

You would like to get partner in to push a Spade through, and you wonder what else he has besides his Spades. No matter, you can deal with this all on your own if you have to. You decide the best attacking lead is the Queen of Diamonds. You are not displeased when dummy goes down and shows you:

      ♠ 7 5 2
      ♡ none
      ◇ A 9 8 7 4
      ♣ A 10 8 6 5

Hal goes into action. He takes the Diamond with the King in his own hand, leads another to dummy's Ace, then ruffs a third Diamond. Now he plays the King of Clubs, leads a Club to dummy's Ace, and ruffs a third Club. So far, he has taken six tricks, and in the process has stripped your hand of everything except your seven trumps.

He now leads a small Spade. You have no option but to ruff it, and feeling a little disgusted you return a trump. Hal takes this, and leads another Spade. Again you have to ruff, and again you must return a trump. For the third time, Hal leads a Spade, and now, thoroughly alarmed, you ruff with the 9, aware that your last two cards are the King and Jack of trumps, and that it's your lead. Hal takes both the last two tricks.

Feeling like someone who has inadvertently swallowed the contents of an over-full ashtray, you watch as your partner solemnly hands over your money to Hal, who equally solemnly thanks you. While the other three make their preparations to leave the train, which is slowing down to enter the station, you anxiously turn out your pockets, and are relieved to find enough small change to get you onto the plane.

Dismally, you make your way along the corridor, and as the train comes to a halt, you step out onto the platform. On your way to the exit barrier, you take a last look round, and what do you see? Hal is busy sharing out the money with the other members of the gang, and they are chortling their way into the bar, where they are going to celebrate the success of one of the oldest tricks ever played on the innocent in the history of card games.

You have just been the latest in the long line of victims of the notorious Mississippi Heart Hand, created about a century ago in order to fleece hapless whist players on the old steamboats, and still perpetrated on any bridge player gullible enough to have the hand planted on him without knowing it. In all its sinister glory, the full hand is:

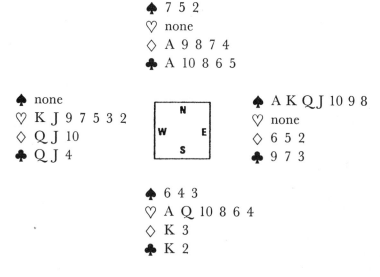

♠ 7 5 2
♡ none
◇ A 9 8 7 4
♣ A 10 8 6 5

♠ none
♡ K J 9 7 5 3 2
◇ Q J 10
♣ Q J 4

♠ A K Q J 10 9 8
♡ none
◇ 6 5 2
♣ 9 7 3

♠ 6 4 3
♡ A Q 10 8 6 4
◇ K 3
♣ K 2

So if you must play bridge with strangers on a train, at any rate beware when one of them goes to the bathroom just before his turn to deal!

On Trial

Bob Laverick pushed his empty plate away, gazed ruminatively round the living room of his bachelor apartment, then asked himself aloud: "Ellington or Bach?"

Before he could supply himself with an answer, there was a ring at the doorbell. Going to the spyhole, he peered through, then gasped with surprise. Quickly he unlatched the chain, and cried:

"Paul! What a rare pleasure. Come right in."

Paul Duveen shook hands, grinned, and entered. He looked around appreciatively.

"This is cozy, Bob. And so tidy. I'd forgotten that anyone's living room could be as neat as this. I've got diapers all over the place, pieces of jigsaw puzzles on every table, toys scientifically placed on the floor so that there's no way to avoid tripping on at least one of them; and enough noise to make a cage full of hungry lions blush for shame."

"You shouldn't have joined," smiled Bob. "I'll grant you there are plenty of times when I envy guys like you, sitting in the middle of a huge gushing fountain of affection, but when I got to 30, I knew I'd never make it. It's the quiet life for me. When you came up just now, I was trying to figure out what kind of music suited my mood; that's about the biggest problem I have once I step through that door."

"Well, talking about problems," said Paul, easing his tall frame into a chair beside the one that Bob had been occupying, "that's why I came to see you. I think you can help me. Sorry to come without warning, but I had a feeling you wouldn't mind."

Paul Duveen, successful stockbroker, father of five, prominent community leader, was known as somebody to whom other people brought their problems. Bob Laverick felt flattered.

"I can't even begin to guess how I can be of any help," he said as he poured drinks, "but naturally I'll be delighted if I can."

"It's about bridge," started Paul. "As you may know, I'm chairman of the club's selection committee. Next month, the big one's coming up, and the committee met last night to pick the team. What I'm going to tell you now is in strict confidence, and I'm quite sure I can rely on you to respect that." He sipped his drink and looked at Bob, who nodded.

"We have two automatic pairs. The same ones you saw in action when you came to watch our match against the Constellation, as they call themselves. But this tournament coming up next month is a 3-day job, and we must have a third pair. Now that Matt Tilson's bank has moved him away to Head Office it means we have the job of replacing him. His old partner, Johnny Yves, ought to be in. He's as steady as a rock in these big matches. Plenty of class and lots of experience. So you see, Bob, the committee was unanimous about five out of the six. Your name came up. They like you, and they like your game, but they don't know quite enough about it to make up their minds for certain. They can't get together for another meeting before the match, so they left it to me to decide whether to put you in with Johnny."

"Well, thanks, Paul. Of course, I'd jump at the chance. Is that your problem solved?"

"Not altogether. Nobody on the committee, including me,

has had the opportunity of playing either with or against you for a whole evening. We've come up against you in duplicates, of course, but only for a few boards at a time, and that's not the same thing. Your duplicate results have been pretty consistent in the six months you've been at the club, and you've been obviously able to adapt to various partners with success. What the committee wants me to try to decide—entirely on my own—is whether you have the level of technique and judgment we're looking for."

"And how do you propose to do that?"

"I thought you'd never ask." Paul grinned. "I'm going to take a hell of a liberty, Bob, and I hope you'll forgive me, but there's only one way I could think of: Let's assume that you and Johnny are playing as a pair; assume that together you can handle all the routine stuff: the part scores, the lay-down games, the straightforward defence. As I see it, these matches turn on the swing hands, and most of the swing hands turn on judgment and technique. Now, you know Johnny. Methodical. Keeps a record of any hand that stretches his mind, and goes over it afterwards to see what more he can learn. Now we come to the liberty. I brought a couple of those hands along with me. If you feel in the mood, I'll turn you loose on them. If not, just tell me."

"What choice do I have? OK, I'm in the mood."

"Good. Here's the first. You're East. It's Love-all, South deals and opens 3 NT. That shows a 24–26 point balanced hand. North raises to 4 NT, which is quantitative. South passes. Your partner leads the 6 of Spades, and this is what you see:

                    DUMMY
            ♠ Q 9 2
            ♡ 10 3
            ◇ Q J 10 9 8
            ♣ J 8 5
                                        EAST
                                ♠ A 8 7 3
                                ♡ 6
                                ◇ 7 4 2
                                ♣ K 10 7 4 3

"South calls for dummy's Queen. Two questions for you:
first, do you play the Ace? Secondly, if you do, what comes
next?"

Bob hunched himself forward, frowning at the paper on
which the diagram was sketched out.

"Take your time," said Paul. "As much as you like. At the
table, I'm sure you'd give it plenty of thought, so give it
plenty now."

After not more than a minute, Bob said: "I play low."

"Good," said Paul. "Mind telling me why?"

"First, my partner can't have more than 3 points, so the
lead can't be 4th highest unless South holds the doubleton
5, 4 only. I'm entitled to assume he's not that crazy. Now, this
contract is going to depend on the Diamond suit. If South
has Ace, King and another Diamond, he's home. Missing one
of the tops, it must surely be the King, in which case, he may
need an entry to dummy later. So I hang on to my Ace for
that reason and see what develops. But there's also the chance
that he's got just the Ace King doubleton, plus the 10 and
Jack of Spades. In that case, I solve his entry problems for him
by playing my Ace. Like I said, Paul, I play low."

"Beautifully reasoned," beamed Paul. "In the match from which Johnny got this hand, we did actually defend against 4 NT. West led the 6 of Spades, the Queen went up, East played low and the contract went one down. At the other table, our North-South pair took a more optimistic view of their cards—and of course they play a 1 Club system which gives them much more room to explore on that kind of hand— and they finished in 6 NT. Now that you know what East holds, there's no point in asking you to shut it out of your mind, but just out of interest, tell me how you would go about making 6 NT as South on the same lead. Take a look at the whole picture:"

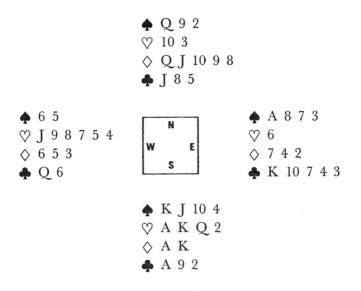

♠ Q 9 2
♡ 10 3
◇ Q J 10 9 8
♣ J 8 5

♠ 6 5
♡ J 9 8 7 5 4
◇ 6 5 3
♣ Q 6

♠ A 8 7 3
♡ 6
◇ 7 4 2
♣ K 10 7 4 3

♠ K J 10 4
♡ A K Q 2
◇ A K
♣ A 9 2

Bob studied the layout for a minute, then said: "This is not specially difficult, Paul. And I hope I'm not flattering myself when I say I think I'd get it right if I were at the table without the benefit of seeing all the hands. I can say that because there's a 100 per cent safety play. Play low from dummy on the opening lead. If East is unwise enough to go up with his Ace, the hand is over. If he plays low, I win with the King. Now I get my two top Diamonds out of the way, then lead the Jack of Spades to dummy's Queen. If the Ace wins, I can get back to dummy by playing the 4 to the 9 on the table. I make 3 Spade tricks, 3 Hearts, 5 Diamonds and the Ace of Clubs."

"Great, Bob. I'm beginning to feel good, and it's not your little mixture in this glass, either. Now, I have just one more for you to look at. Before I show it to you, I'd like to ask you if you've ever played with Johnny Yves."

"Only once, Paul. And we got along quite well. He's a fine bridge player."

"Yes, he is. And he leaves the fireworks to the others. You can believe what he bids, and you can trust what he plays in defence. Now here's a hand for you; I want you to imagine that Johnny's North; you're South; game to your side only; Johnny deals and opens 1 Spade. These are your cards:"

♠ K
♡ K J 9 7 5 3
♢ Q 10 9 2
♣ K Q

"Over Johnny's 1 Spade, what is your bid? Opponents silent, by the way."

"No problem there. I bid 2 Hearts."

"Johnny then says 2 Spades."

"Disappointing, but not the end of the world. There should be game somewhere. I keep things rolling with 3 Diamonds."

"Well, I can tell you that if you did, he'd bid 4 Diamonds."

"Mm. Let's see where we've got to here. Johnny has a

minimum hand in terms of high card points; he has no tolerance for Hearts; he has 5 Spades for sure, but I feel inclined to place him with 6; and to raise Diamonds at this level, he's going to have four of them to an honor, maybe two honors. So he has very few cards in Hearts and Clubs, and practically no top cards in those suits. That's probably the reason he by-passed 3 NT so readily, and that's the reason I'm not looking for a No Trump contract myself. I can see 3 probable losers, so I'm not looking for a 5 Diamond contract. So I'm left with a 2-way proposition: pass 4 Diamonds or try 4 Spades. I've got the stuff; Johnny will be glad to see the King of trumps, and I'd be surprised if there are four losers in the hands. I make it about a 60–40 shot, and at Teams, I've got to bid my vulnerable games with that percentage of optimism. OK, Paul, I've made up my mind. I bid 4 Spades. How near the target was I?"

For answer, a delighted Paul Duveen laid out the full hand:

(See next page)

"Just about a perfect analysis, Bob. In our last match, our opponents bid 1 Spade, 2 Hearts, 2 Spades, then the South player plunged with 3 NT. He got a Club lead, and then had to decide whether to run for 8 tricks and concede 1 down, or put his money on the Diamond finesse, with a chance of 2 overtricks if it came off. He ran the Queen of Diamonds; our East player won with the King, then we peeled off our 4 Club tricks, followed by the Ace of Hearts. 2 down.

"At the other table, Matt Tilson held your cards, and we got to 4 Spades, which is an easy make."

Paul rose and stretched himself.

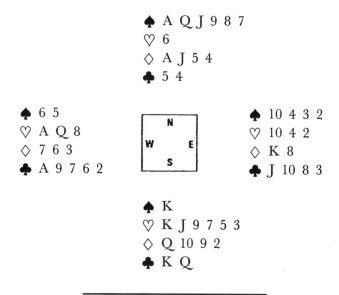

♠ A Q J 9 8 7
♡ 6
◇ A J 5 4
♣ 5 4

♠ 6 5
♡ A Q 8
◇ 7 6 3
♣ A 9 7 6 2

N
W E
S

♠ 10 4 3 2
♡ 10 4 2
◇ K 8
♣ J 10 8 3

♠ K
♡ K J 9 7 5 3
◇ Q 10 9 2
♣ K Q

"I'm off for home now," he said. "I pass Johnny's place on the way, and I think I'll just drop by and tell him the good news. Welcome to the team, Bob; it's good news for me, too."

The Ultimate Gamble

The whole strange affair really began with a chance remark on the way to the 16th green. J.B. Coghill strolled along in the brilliant West Indian sunshine with Manny Steinberg at his side. Both men were presidents of large companies, and they both liked to fly off to the sunny warmth of the Caribbean whenever the pressures of their business lives eased off for a day or two.

"Playing much bridge these days, J.B.?" asked Manny.

"Not much. Duplicate bores me, and I frankly don't care to play rubber bridge for small stakes. It's not all that often that I can get into a game where the stakes are high enough to interest me."

Manny gave his companion a quizzical look.

"What's high?"

"The sky's the limit for me. What's high for you?"

Manny just shrugged and smiled. They had reached the green, and there were other things to be attended to.

Back in the States a few days later, the phone rang in Coghill's plush office early in the evening.

"That you, J.B.?"

"Yeah. Manny?"

"Right. Listen, J.B., this is about bridge. There are three of us down here at my place who'd like to take you up on this high-stake bit. The other two are sharp boys, neat players, so it won't be a waste of your time. How high are you prepared to go?"

62

"Like I told you; the sky's the limit."

"Well, J.B., you just drop what you're doing; it's quitting time anyway. Come on over to my place. We've got something going with sky written all over it. See you in about twenty minutes. And bring your cheque book."

As Coghill rode the elevator to his friend's penthouse, he wondered what kind of bridge game he had let himself in for. He had boasted often enough that the sky was the limit. Did he really mean that? Well, it was too late to worry about it now. Sharp boys, eh? What's Manny up to?

"Come in, J.B.," said Manny's voice, and the door opened. The sharp boys turned out to be as old as Manny and himself, and after brief introductions, Manny put forward his proposition.

"I understand you guys like a bit of spice with your bridge, right? Good. So do I. Well, this should make it real spicy. We'll play just four hands, like Chicago, except that it'll be game-all each deal. Scoring the same as duplicate, but honors to count. The stakes will be $100 a point . . ."

A long pause. Then J.B. said: "Did I hear right?"

"You did. $100 a point."

"So 3 NT bid and made would rate $60,000."

"Right."

"And a Grand Slam bid and made pulls in around $200,000."

"Thereabouts."

"Manny, this is the damnedest idea."

"What do you say, J.B.?"

"Don't rush me, Manny."

J. B. Coghill was torn between greed and panic. This was real high-stake bridge all right. There was big money to be made in a very short time. And lost, too. Four losing hands in a row might cost . . . He was suddenly aware that the others were looking intently at him. Abruptly he snapped, "Make it just one hand instead of four, and you're on."

It was agreed. They cut for partners. Then nearly twenty minutes went by while each pair checked and double-checked every piece of bidding mechanism, and all defensive leads and signals. Perhaps after all this the hand will be thrown in, thought J.B. What a farce that would be. Then another thought came to him: there might be a Grand Slam in the cards, but against him. How could he explain to his family, his business associates and his friends that he was selling the house, the farm and most of his stocks just on account of one hand of bridge?

"This is crazy," he said to himself, "but you were the one who kept on insisting on high stakes. Now you got them." His mouth was drier than he could ever remember.

Looking back on the affair afterwards, he could scarcely recall dealing, but he must have dealt, because he vividly remembered the moment he picked up his cards. His heart leapt. He had a big hand.

♠ 3
♡ A K Q J 7 5 2
◇ 4 2
♣ A K Q

J.B. and his partner had decided to play one of the Big Club systems, so, heart still pounding, he opened the bidding with 1 Club. His left-hand opponent, without a flicker of expression or the slightest trace of hesitation, bid 4 Spades. J.B.'s partner passed. And now his right-hand opponent bid 5 Spades.

"Let there be an urgent telephone call for me this very

instant, and let it demand that I leave here immediately," prayed J.B. But the phone remained silent. The whole room was silent, but it was a silence that throbbed with fierce excitement.

J.B. was doing some mental arithmetic, his face creased into a map of worry and uncertainty. "If they make 5 Spades, it'll cost me $65,000. What are my chances in defence? On that bidding I can't expect to make any Heart tricks at all. Can I rely on making all the three top Clubs? Not very well. So they can make 5 Spades as far as I can see. What happens if I go on to 6 Hearts? The first thing to happen is that some joker will double. OK, let's say 2 down at worst. That'll cost me $50,000. Seems I don't have any choice."

In a gravedigger's voice, he said "6 Hearts." However, to his great relief, nobody doubled, and there was no more bidding. The King of Spades was led, and the full deal was:

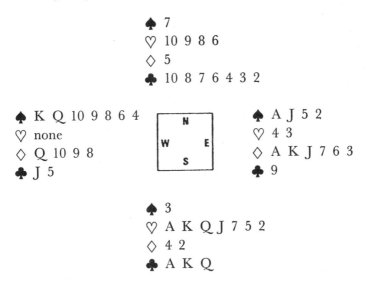

```
              ♠ 7
              ♡ 10 9 8 6
              ◊ 5
              ♣ 10 8 7 6 4 3 2

♠ K Q 10 9 8 6 4    ┌─────────┐    ♠ A J 5 2
♡ none              │    N    │    ♡ 4 3
◊ Q 10 9 8          │ W     E │    ◊ A K J 7 6 3
♣ J 5               │    S    │    ♣ 9
                    └─────────┘
              ♠ 3
              ♡ A K Q J 7 5 2
              ◊ 4 2
              ♣ A K Q
```

The King of Spades was overtaken by the Ace, and in almost the same movement, East's Ace of Diamonds was pushed halfway through the table for the setting trick.

"One down and 100 for honors," panted J.B. "All square."

From someone came a gentle chuckle. Then another man began to giggle. Soon they were all laughing, and the laughter mounted and erupted and exploded, and they were all laying back in their chairs and braying like drunken donkeys. Eventually they quietened down, and Manny bid J.B. goodnight.

Sitting in his car, J.B. found himself sweating profusely. He drove off carefully, aware that his legs were none too strong and his hands were trembling. Halfway home, he was suddenly hit by a thought. He pulled over to the side of the road and braked his car to a halt.

"Hell, they had 6 Spades cold. Nobody mentioned it, not even the sharp boys. And nobody doubled my 6 Hearts. That doesn't add up. I didn't notice it myself, I guess, but I was in no state to notice anything after the hand was over. But those sharp boys, and even old Manny, so quick to analyze . . . My God, I think they had the whole thing rigged somehow. Perhaps they were going to play four rigged hands. Now why should they do that?"

He continued to worry about it for days afterwards, but nobody gave him any help or enlightenment. The only change that was noticeable was the spectacle of J.B. playing rubber bridge quite contentedly for 2 cents a point.

A Breadtime Story

There once lived a very handsome, impeccably dressed and exquisitely mannered young man called Max. He was deeply sun-tanned all the year round, which was not surprising, as he spent most of his time at such popular playgrounds as Acapulco, Montego Bay, Estoril, Capri and Nassau.

Max loved fun and adventure, and hated the mere idea of work. As a matter of fact, he was careful to avoid any mention of this distasteful topic. Ever since he had first discovered his ability to play bridge just that bit better than most other players, he had made a decision to live by playing rather than working, and over the years he had also cultivated the elegant air of indolence which was now as natural to him as his unaffected charm of personality.

It had not been easy in those early days. As a fledgling money-bridge pro, he had found that he lost nearly as often as he won; it was only with great difficulty that he was able to pay his bills and fly off to the next watering-place. The reasons were not hard to find, and once found, taught him some valuable lessons.

He discovered that the good players frequently had to suffer. Other good players stiffened up their game when playing against him. Lesser players went to pieces when partnering him; they became nervous and flustered and would either hoist him into unmakeable contracts as a form of flattery or fail to break enemy contracts because they were looking for some esoteric defence instead of doing the easy and obvious.

Max then made another useful discovery. After studying the pros at work, he saw that they often hunted in threes. They would play set with a wealthy fourth, even though he might be a thoroughly poor player, correctly figuring that, provided the session lasted long enough, each of them would play against Mr. Rich twice for every once they had to partner him. And that way a handsome harvest could be reaped for all.

So Max set about building himself an attractive façade. His bridge-playing half would be a cheerful lamb looking eagerly for the slaughterhouse. He would wander into the high-stake room of a club, sit at a respectful distance from the action, and exude his impressive air of well-bred naiveté. At the same time, he would be soaking up information at a furious rate. When he was ready, he would allow himself to be reluctantly persuaded to take part in a rubber, usually at the highest permissible stakes, and sometimes a bit higher than that.

Under normal circumstances, the pros would find this stranger to be rich pickings. But circumstances never seemed quite normal when Max was the stranger at the table. Despite pathetically inept bidding on his part and a series of apparently lucky plays, it appeared at the end of the session that he was the sole winner while the other three tried to hide their mortified feelings while they fished out their bankrolls (Max always played strictly for cash). He would then happily disclaim any credit for this incomprehensible swing of fate's pendulum, and after apologizing profusely for his inadequacies as a bridge player he would saunter off to spend his winnings.

Max was not often short of "bread"—as the young people sometimes refer to money—but when he was, well there was usually a high-stake game not too far away. He once told me of an occasion when he had made some recklessly extravagant presents to one of his more attractive female companions, and had needed to climb back into solvency again. He found the local bridge club, sat around for half an hour while he made mental notes of as many peculiarities, traits, whims and behavioral patterns as he could, then politely asked whether a stranger might be allowed to play.

"I'm afraid I'm not really in your class, gentlemen," he said with his disarming deference, "but I'll do my best. I'd sure appreciate it if you'd tell me when I do anything wrong."

The three men he was addressing smiled hungrily. They, too, were pros, and they were also short of bread. After the cut, Max sat opposite a man whom he had diagnosed as having basically sound judgment, but who was given to bursts of impetuosity now and again. On Max's left sat an opinionated bore who had a rigid outlook on the game, with no flair and little imagination. On Max's right was a quiet and thoughtful player, who could be really dangerous.

The first rubber was uneventful. Max took things quietly; the cards were good to him, and he jogged without strain to a winning score, casually overlooking the overtrick here and there. But he was not even halfway to restoring his depleted supply of bread. Somebody suggested that they keep the same partners, and the second rubber began. Again things went smoothly for Max. The scores piled up on the We side of his scorepad. He and his partner then made 2 NT to score a tactically precious 70. They took three penalties in rapid succession as their opponents strove to outbid them. After that, they were allowed to get the other 30 without interference, and thus became vulnerable.

Max's opponents were now even more inclined to stretch their necks. Max knew that there was little risk in bidding one more than the cards warranted, because his opponents were now determined to save the rubber at any price, which was exactly the price Max had in mind. Finally, at considerable cost, the opponents broke through, and it was game-all.

It was then that Max, sitting South, picked up:

♠ Q 10 9 7 5
♡ A 7 2
◇ 10 2
♣ A J 2

West dealt and opened 1 NT. North passed. East bid 2♡. "No sense in interfering here," thought Max; "2 Hearts won't hurt us."

West passed his partner's weak response, but North then stepped into the picture with a double. East gave this careful thought then bid 3♡.

"Partner has some useful bits and pieces over there, maybe as much as 8 or 9 points; void or singleton in Hearts, and just can't bear to go quietly," reasoned Max. It was most unlikely that there would be more than 5 losers between the two hands. He bid 3♠. "I can't see West doubling that," he said to himself.

West did indeed refrain from doubling, but instead bid 4♡. North, with the bit firmly between his teeth now, galloped on to 4♠. After two passes, West doubled, and there was no further bidding. West led the King of Hearts, and the full deal was:

(See next page)

"Things could be worse," mused Max as he studied the dummy, "although if I get away with this I'm not going to risk any more rubbers with that character. A few more bids like

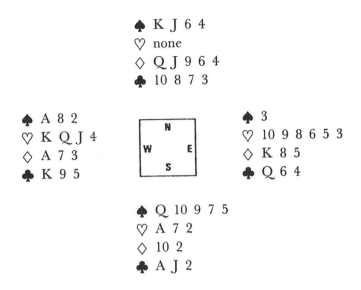

♠ K J 6 4
♡ none
◇ Q J 9 6 4
♣ 10 8 7 3

♠ A 8 2
♡ K Q J 4
◇ A 7 3
♣ K 9 5

♠ 3
♡ 10 9 8 6 5 3
◇ K 8 5
♣ Q 6 4

♠ Q 10 9 7 5
♡ A 7 2
◇ 10 2
♣ A J 2

The bidding had been:

W	N	E	S
1 NT	pass	2♡	pass
pass	dble	3♡	3♠
4♡	4♠	pass	pass
dble	pass	pass	pass

those last two and he'd ruin me. Now, let me see. There's the
Ace of Spades and the two top Diamonds to lose. Can I set up
those Diamonds before somebody switches to Clubs?"

He saw that the risk of drawing trumps early was that the
defender with the Ace might return a Club and inevitably sink
the boat. But if he tried to set up Diamond tricks before going
for the trumps, the defence might well realize why he was
delaying his attack on trumps, and make the Club switch even

more imperative. Plus the lesser risk of running into a Diamond ruff. But he felt it had to be done.

West surely had the Ace of Spades. Max felt he could rely on that stolid and unimaginative nature he had seen in action previously. If the Club honors were divided, Max felt certain that it would not occur to West to open up the suit from an unguarded honor. There was one big obstacle to negotiate, and Max plunged in.

He ruffed the Heart in dummy, then led a small Diamond, East playing the 5, Max the 10 and West the Ace. West frowned long and hard at the Heart void in dummy, then led the Ace and another trump, Max winning in his own hand. Now came another Diamond to dummy's Queen and East's King. And back—straight back—came a Club.

"Too late, too late!" whooped Max exultantly to himself, but his expression lost none of its composure as he played the Ace of Clubs. Then he crossed to dummy with a Spade, thereby picking up West's last trump at the same time, and cashed three good Diamonds.

"Well, bless my soul!" he exclaimed in great surprise. "Partner, the rest are ours. I must have been lucky somewhere."

East knew full well who was to blame. East knew that he should have gone up with the King on the first Diamond lead, then pushed a Club through, but East also knew that he had to play bridge with West every day, and besides there was his reputation to consider. East said nothing.

Max pocketed his winnings, pushing a thick wad of notes into his wallet, then turned to the three men sitting morosely at the table.

"Cheer up, gentlemen," he said solicitously, "I've just figured out how that last hand suddenly worked out so well for me. It was just that lucky little 10 of Diamonds. Well, it sure was good of you to put up with a broken-down player like me. Such a lucky one, too. Thanks."

Later that night, as he locked the door of his hotel room and went over to the icebox to get out the champagne, his current girl-friend's eyes opened wide as she saw the large ornate bottle being produced for her inspection.

"All this and champagne too? You're turning a young girl's head."

When the glasses were filled, she asked, "What are we drinking to?"

Max started to voice a highly erotic thought, then he remembered how much the champagne had cost him, and his mind went back a few hours.

"Here's a toast to the 10 of Diamonds," he said.

Nether Regional

The Devil fidgeted nervously with his pitchfork. "There's another one of those bridge players on his way down," he said, "and you know what trouble-makers they are."

He scanned the dossier with a worried frown. "He's got the usual list of sins, but I don't like the look of this last item: it says he shot his partner for not returning his suit. That's the kind of resident we can do without."

Turning to his companion, he said: "Better get things set up here. We'll give him Hand No. 87. That ought to knock some of the nonsense out of him. Come to think of it, I'll partner him myself. Let him try to shoot me."

Shortly afterwards, Arnold appeared, chewing vigorously and gazing around with an air of critical disapproval. Going up to the Devil, he said: "Why don't you put the air-conditioning on? This kind of atmosphere don't help a guy to concentrate on his game. And all this smoke and stuff. You fellers never heard of pollution?"

The Devil made a mental note to see that the temperature was notched up a degree or two and to give the workers in the sulphur plant instructions to make even yellower and thicker smoke. But he managed a smile, and said: "I suppose you're all ready for a game?"

"Natch," answered Arnold. "My last partner told me to go to hell, and since I'm here, I might as well see how you guys operate with the cards. If it turns out you're all in bad shape, leave it to poppa. I'll get a clinic going, and before you know where you are we'll be beating the pants off those smug johnnies upstairs. Case of paradise lost, eh?" He brayed at his own joke.

"Come," said the Devil, who had seen nothing to laugh at.

Two mournful characters appeared, and took their places at a table. The Devil pointed: "That's the South seat," he said. "I'll put you there, and I shall be your partner."

"Putting me in the hot seat," he said, again laughing immoderately, though nobody else seemed to appreciate the point.

In a blur of sulphur the cards were dealt, and Arnold found himself with:

♠ A Q J 9 6
♡ K
♢ A K
♣ A Q 7 6 4

Arnold started to gloat over this mouth-watering collection, but after a few seconds a fleeting spasm of recognition twitched at the back of his mind; he had seen this lot before somewhere. He thought hard for some moments, but nothing surfaced. He shrugged, and concentrated on the bidding, which went:

SOUTH	NORTH
2♣	2 NT
3♠	4♠
5♣	5♡
6♢	6♠

Arnold felt a strong urge to go on to 7 Spades, but the same odd feeling that he was re-treading old ground deterred him. He passed, and the Devil, after giving him a hard look soon sat back complacently. This little experience ought to bring him into line, mused the Devil, and we've got plenty more where this came from. As he well knew, the full hand was:

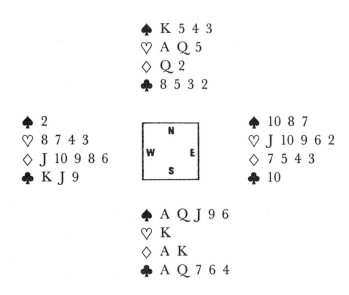

```
                    ♠ K 5 4 3
                    ♡ A Q 5
                    ◊ Q 2
                    ♣ 8 5 3 2

♠ 2                      N            ♠ 10 8 7
♡ 8 7 4 3                             ♡ J 10 9 6 2
◊ J 10 9 8 6        W       E         ◊ 7 5 4 3
♣ K J 9                 S             ♣ 10

                    ♠ A Q J 9 6
                    ♡ K
                    ◊ A K
                    ♣ A Q 7 6 4
```

The Jack of Diamonds was led, and after winning the trick Arnold surveyed his prospects.

"Good thing we kept out of 7," he said cheerfully. The Devil glared at him, but was immediately assuaged by the thought that Arnold was due to go down in 6.

The King of Hearts was cashed, then the other Diamond. Next, Arnold played the Ace and Queen of trumps, then over to dummy's King. Dummy's Hearts were cashed, which left the remaining cards like this:

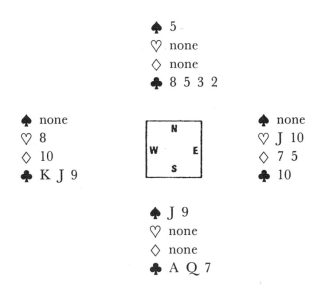

```
              ♠ 5
              ♡ none
              ◇ none
              ♣ 8 5 3 2

♠ none          ┌─────────┐          ♠ none
♡ 8             │    N    │          ♡ J 10
◇ 10            │ W     E │          ◇ 7 5
♣ K J 9         │    S    │          ♣ 10
                └─────────┘
              ♠ J 9
              ♡ none
              ◇ none
              ♣ A Q 7
```

Arnold stole a glance at the complacent faces around him. He had to avoid losing 2 Club tricks, but how was he going to do that?

"Hell!" he said aloud.

"Correct," said the Devil with a thin-lipped smile.

"Well, out of evil cometh forth good," said Arnold defiantly, and the others blanched and quailed back.

He played a Club from dummy, and when East supplied the 10, Arnold played low, cackling horribly as he did so. East, who had begun to lose interest in the hand, suddenly sat up and looked distraught. West, who had not yet played, looked baffled. Eventually they had to give in. Either a Club lead from West if he overtook, or a ruff and discard from either side would see Arnold safely home.

"Nice work, you guys," said Arnold sardonically. "First you try to put the fix on me by planting a hand that figures to go down. Then you try to con me into bidding 7. Next, you expect me to play the hand like a kid in Sunday School"—heavy tremors passed through East and West—"and finally you don't even do your homework properly. If you take the trouble to check on that cute little number we've just played, you'll find it came up in the Summer Nationals around 1959. And guess who sat South—yours truly, of course. Now let me tell you what I would have done in your place."

"In my place? This is my place," broke in the Devil sternly. "I'm in charge here. Sort of Torment Director, you might say."

"The Devil you are," said Arnold.

"The Devil I sure am," replied the Devil. "Now you can help me rig up a misfit, since you're so smart. There's trouble on the way down. You bridge players are bad enough, but this next one's a bridge writer. They're the worst of the lot."

The Unreachable Contract

Alan saw him coming and tried to veer away out of range, but it was too late. The Bore had spotted him, and when The Bore spotted you there was no escape. With a thinly disguised sigh of resignation, Alan allowed himself to be grasped firmly by the elbow and propelled towards the bar. Well, he would get a free drink out of this, but at what cost? The last time he'd got trapped, he remembered, the extrication job had taken every bit of half an hour.

As the drinks arrived, the inevitable tatty scrap of paper was produced from The Bore's pocket and laid out carefully on the table. Then one corner of it was torn off and turned so that Alan could see it. The larger piece went back into The Bore's pocket.

"Club duplicate last night," he said, "and a perfect example of how to reach the unreachable contract."

"What's an unreachable contract, in your definition?"

"One that can't be reached using ordinary methods. And yet we had the perfect contract on our cards. I don't see one pair in fifty getting there. Maybe less than that. You don't believe me, eh?"

"Not yet I don't, no."

Alan was a member of the celebrated Wanderers squad, a sextet of amateur bridge players who toured the world at vacation time at their own expense, challenging whoever would take them on. They prided themselves on the accuracy of their bidding, and they felt—as Alan did at that moment—

that if a contract were in the cards, somehow it could be bid. With a slightly greater show of interest, Alan said: "Show me this marvel of yours."

"I'll show you just part of it to start with," said The Bore with his usual deviousness. "Here's the South hand. N–S are vul; West dealt and bid 1 Spade. North and East both pass. Your bid."

♠ 10 2
♡ Q 10 4 3
◇ A Q 9 4
♣ K Q 7

Alan studied the hand for a few moments. "I double," he said. "I clearly have enough for a double in the balancing position."

"Just so," agreed The Bore. "Now, over your double, West bids 2 Spades. Partner thinks for a long time, then says 3 Diamonds."

"Who was your partner?"

"Barney Wilkes. You know, the car leasing business."

"Yes, I know him. A fairly reliable bidder."

"Barney's OK. But he didn't bid 3 Diamonds. Your partners would, I'm sure. So proceed on that basis."

Alan thought: partner has a few points, a sketchy Diamond suit, no tolerance for Hearts; what's the catch?

"I probably pass," he said.

"I thought so!" exclaimed The Bore triumphantly. "Barney and I got a whale of a top on this one. Look, here's the deal."

He produced the rest of the hand and put the two pieces of paper together. This is what Alan saw.

♠ A Q 4 3
♡ K
◇ J 10 8 2
♣ 8 6 5 2

♠ K J 9 8 6 5
♡ A J 6
◇ 6 3
♣ A 3

♠ 7
♡ 9 8 7 5 2
◇ K 7 5
♣ J 10 9 4

♠ 10 2
♡ Q 10 4 3
◇ A Q 9 4
♣ K Q 7

"So where's the fantastic score on that one?" asked Alan. "Don't tell me nobody else got to 3 Diamonds?"

"A lot of them did," said The Bore smugly. "Here's how we bid it."

W	N	E	S
1♠	pass	pass	dble
2♠	dble	pass	3♡
pass	3♠	pass	3 NT
pass	pass	pass	

"Nice bidding, eh? Barney's double was responsive, at least in our methods. I had to try 3 Hearts in case we had a fit there; now when he bids 3 Spades, I know he has a good Spade stop and no Hearts worth mentioning, but some useful cards in at least one of the minors. 3 NT is a terrific spot, but I repeat you can't get there using rigid system bids. We were the only pair to play in 3 NT."

Alan's expression had taken on a faint tinge of distaste.

"Finish the story," he said. "What happened in 3 NT?"

"Well, West led the 7 of Spades, which I ran to my 10. I led a Heart. West took his Ace and led another Spade to dummy's Queen. Now I ran the Jack of Diamonds. Once I had set up my 4 Diamond tricks, I played the King of Clubs, which West won. He led another Spade, of course, but by that time I had 4 Diamonds, 3 Spades, a Heart and a Club for 9 tricks and a clear top. No problem. Some hand, eh?"

"There's just the chance I might be tempted to bid it that way against third-class opposition," said Alan coldly. "But I must say I'd far sooner defend against 3 NT from the West seat than play it from your seat."

"What do you mean?"

"I mean this: to break the contract, I must obviously bring in my Spade suit. I'm going to be on lead 3 times. First with the opening lead, then twice more with my two Aces. That means I must clear the suit in two leads in order to run it when I get in for the third time. Now, how are the Spades divided, assuming East has at least one?"

Alan took out a pencil and started scribbling.

'A'	'B'	'C'	'D'
A 10 x x	Q 10 x x	A Q x x	Q x x x
Q x	A x	10 x	A 10

"In 'A' and 'B', with the 10 in the hand with the long Spades, I can't win. In 'C' and 'D', I can kill the 10 on the second lead, provided I start with the King on the opening lead. And since the only way I can win anyway is to lead the King, that's what I would lead at the table, I assure you. As the cards actually lie on this hand, I get the Spades going before you can set up your 9 tricks. Try it for yourself. Ace of Spades on my King, then a Heart to my Ace; now the Jack of Spades, which kills your 10, and which dummy wins with the Queen. You can set up your 4 Diamond tricks, but I just sit back and wait to get in with the Ace of Clubs, and then, my friend, you've had it."

The Bore was crestfallen. Alan got to his feet and stretched.

"Who wants to bend his brain getting to an unreachable contract which is also unmakeable?" he said. "But thanks for the drink."

The Edge of Madness

My first year as a bridge player was a period of utter confusion. I sat and watched as my professional colleagues played, and was occasionally allowed to join in. But everybody who became my partner expected different things from me, and sometimes these expectations were expressed as demands, not to be lightly ignored. As I gradually strove to impose some logical pattern of my own on the seemingly endless and random permutations of bidding and play, I noticed also that men you thought you really knew well would occasionally undergo a frightening sea-change. I especially remember two middle-aged men who worked side by side and—or so I thought—enjoyed the most harmonious relationship. Their conversation was usually lit by little flashes of witty banter, and they were good company. But at the table one day, one of them, towards the end of a hand, was puzzling which card to play. The other, who was his left-hand opponent, leaned over and started to pluck a card from his hand, saying something like: "It doesn't matter what you do." To my amazement, a ferocious snarl followed from the man who was trying to decide what to play, and the words, uttered in a tone close to hatred: "Don't you tell me how to play my cards!"

They didn't have a civil word to say to one another for a long while after that. I put it down to the strain of a rough day, but before long I noticed that beneath the surface of even the most placid natures there lurked the most unexpected demons, and that the bridge table was the natural habitat of these monsters.

After a few months, I joined a small bridge club in the locality where I lived, where the atmosphere was usually friendly, although a whole evening which went by without its share of bitter recriminations was a rarity. Were things any better at the big-name bridge clubs up in town? I asked a few questions and got some straight answers, which rather depressed me. There was one particular club which had a bad reputation: the stakes were about ten times higher than those I usually played for, and not only were the members not very good players, but things actually got quite out of hand now and again. My curiosity was aroused.

A few months later I decided to celebrate my first anniversary as a bridge player by spending an evening at this notorious club. I took with me all the money I could lay hands on, in case my luck deserted me, arrived at the club, signed the visitors' book, hung up my old raincoat in the lobby, and went into the card room.

As it happened, my luck was in that night. The bidding and play were indeed crude at times, even compared with the rustic standards of my local club, but I kept my head and prospered steadily. Not so one of the members, a man in his thirties, broad-shouldered and bony, a shaven head, deep-set staring eyes in a sallow face, and an accent that belonged somewhere in Eastern Europe. His partner at my table was a much younger man, quietly dressed in a suit of office grey, quietly spoken, very deferential. He was patently out of his depth in this company, and was nervously aware of it. His hands shook slightly as he held his cards, and his brow glistened with sweat.

My own partner was an older man of slow and ponderous ways and occasional lapses of memory, but the two of us had little real work to do in the early part of the rubber except defend with the minimum of mistakes, as our opponents were over-bidding atrociously. The man with the Eastern European accent had apparently lost more than he wanted to lose, and was determined to get it back. His partner was too cowed to do anything except tag along. After we bid and made a game contract, they became even more indiscreet with their competitive bids, and we collected a few more useful penalties. Then their luck changed, they made game, and the stage was set for the final scene.

While the scores were being entered for that hand, I became aware that my incipient head-cold was not far off, and that my nose would soon be giving me some trouble. After reaching in my pocket for a handkerchief, I remembered that I'd left it in my raincoat. I excused myself, and went into the lobby. Walking up to my battered and creased old coat, I plunged my hand into the pocket, and to my astonishment made contact with what was obviously a gun. I took a look around. Nobody about. I took out the gun and wonderingly examined it. It was a Luger, big, shiny, powerful, and deadly. Why should anyone want to plant a gun on me? I stuck it into my waistbelt while I continued to search for my handkerchief. It wasn't there.

Then suddenly the thought hit me. Wrong coat. A few pegs further along I found my own coat, got my handkerchief, but left the Luger in my waistbelt, and with this sinister piece of hardware nudging me in the ribs I went back into the card room.

I found my partner just finishing dealing the following hand from the East seat:

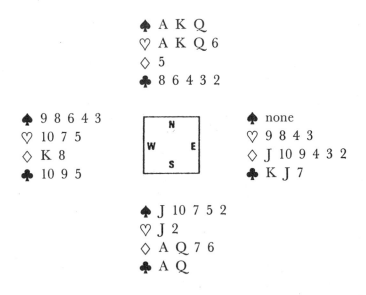

              ♠ A K Q
              ♡ A K Q 6
              ◇ 5
              ♣ 8 6 4 3 2

♠ 9 8 6 4 3   ♠ none
♡ 10 7 5   ♡ 9 8 4 3
◇ K 8   ◇ J 10 9 4 3 2
♣ 10 9 5   ♣ K J 7

              ♠ J 10 7 5 2
              ♡ J 2
              ◇ A Q 7 6
              ♣ A Q

East passed, and South—the nervous young man—opened
1 Spade. After I had passed with the West cards, my volatile
opponent in the North seat must have felt that here was a
heaven-sent opportunity to recoup his entire losses for the
evening in one hand. He went on a bidding rampage, producing
a stream of forcing bids, cue bids and asking bids, and stopping
only when at last the hapless South bid 7 Spades.

The bidding had been incomprehensible to me, and I had
no idea of what to lead, so I took a more or less blind stab with
the 10 of Clubs. My partner played the King, and South won.
He then played dummy's three trumps, my partner parting
with two small Diamonds, then carelessly throwing a Club.
South came to hand with a Club in order to draw my two
remaining trumps. Then came the Jack of Hearts, the Queen
and the King.

As South took dummy's Ace of Hearts from the table, he
was visibly twitching with nervous excitement, and he fre-

quently ran his tongue over his dry lips. Before the Ace of Hearts was played, the position of the cards around the table was:

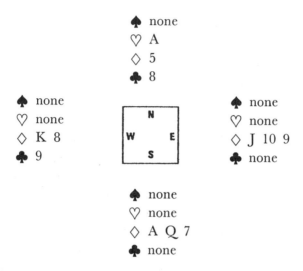

♠ none
♥ A
♦ 5
♣ 8

♠ none
♥ none
♦ K 8
♣ 9

♠ none
♥ none
♦ J 10 9
♣ none

♠ none
♥ none
♦ A Q 7
♣ none

Both East and South discarded Diamonds on the Ace of Hearts, but when it came to my turn to play, I had no idea of what was the best thing to do. It seemed to me that I might be in the grip of what I had heard of as a squeeze, but I wasn't sure because I had quite forgotten whether or not the Jack of Clubs had been played. Did my partner have it? Or had he played it? Did South have it? I didn't know, but I did know that I wasn't prepared to bare my guarded King of Diamonds. Away went the 9 of Clubs.

The Eastern European character in the North seat sat back in his chair, relief written all over his face. But South wasn't reading his partner's face: he was staring glumly at his cards, wondering if fortune was going to favor him with a successful finesse. For South had also forgotten to count the Clubs!

North, who was sprawling happily in his chair, suddenly jerked upright, tense as a steel wire, as South ignored the master Club in dummy and instead reached for the 5 of Diamonds. The finesse lost to my King, and down went the grand slam.

North's face was twisted like an animal in pain. For a few seconds, incredulity and horror gripped him. Then he sprang up, pushing his chair violently and noisily back so that South instinctively flinched in alarm. North seized the 8 of Clubs, leant far across the table, and pushed the card into South's startled face.

"Thirteenth Club!" he shrieked. He tore the card into fragments and strode to the open window, where he hurled the pieces into the night, watching for a moment as they fluttered down towards the London traffic far below. Then he whirled on poor South and in a hysterically loud voice let loose an inarticulate torrent of abuse. At the peak of this tirade, he suddenly broke off and rushed from the room.

I followed. I saw him head straight for his raincoat, a raincoat which looked almost exactly like mine. He went frantically through both pockets over and over again. I saw him pound the wall with his fist in impotent fury. He screamed one last curse, then stalked angrily in the direction of the stairs leading to the street. I never saw him again.

Half an hour later, I stood on Waterloo Bridge, looking down at the murky water, and thinking of the even murkier depths of human nature. Then I threw the Luger into the Thames.

Star of the Archives

Isaac Haufmann let it be known that he was retiring from the world of tournament bridge. He didn't authorize a press release, or indeed make any kind of public statement, but first to one friend and then to another he mentioned that from now on he was going to make do with the occasional game of rubber bridge. He was going on 74, he admitted, and even the normally undemanding local duplicate games brought him the sort of strain he could do without.

Jim Mantini, cub reporter with the Calf City Chronicle, saw the makings of a good story when the news reached him. After all, Calf City was a little short of celebrities, and there weren't too many people like old Isaac around; by reputation alone, he was one of a kind.

He paid a visit to Isaac's suburban home one afternoon and asked politely to be allowed to listen and make a few notes while the old man talked. No objection, said Isaac cheerfully. He liked company, and in his day the press had been good to him.

They went over his career, picking out the highlights; his friendship with Vanderbilt, his feud with Culbertson, his outspoken contempt for the master points system which had nearly cost him his place on the national team. They went over his glittering record in international matches, and he expressed regret at having been too old to joust with the Blue Team.

They spoke of personalities: the giants, the eccentrics, the unapproachables. Jim persuaded Isaac to give him a strictly off-the-record account of the infamous "deliberate revoke" scandal which had rocked the tournament world years ago.

"Any regrets?" asked Jim. "You became a full-time bridge pro on your thirtieth birthday, or so I read, and I also read that you had a brilliant career in public administration ahead of you at the time. Did you do the right thing, as you see it now?"

"At that time, I thought Yes. Now I still think Yes. At any time, Yes, Yes, Yes! People who don't play bridge, or who treat the game as a superficial way of passing the time, don't realize how much richness there is there. I don't mean financial richness, Jim, although I can't complain, myself. But the game is an inexhaustible source of rich experiences, vivid, intense, satisfying to a quite amazing degree. You probably don't know what I'm talking about, but ask any worn-out old pro like me, and he'll tell you the same thing. Believe me, it's kept me going for nearly half a century."

"You must have played something like half a million hands," said Jim, who had gone to the trouble of working out the probable figure, and knew he wasn't too far out. "Is there any one hand which you remember more vividly than all the rest?"

"It may surprise you to know that I don't have a good memory for hands once they've been played," replied Isaac. "My memory's pretty patchy these days anyway. But one hand—out of all that great mass of hands? Let me see . . . Yes, there was a hand, a long, long time ago . . ." He paused, a far-away look came into his eyes, and his face settled into an expression of such mellow rapture that Jim's curiosity was aroused.

"Must have been a sensation," he ventured.

"In its way it was. Wait a minute. I've got a record of it here somewhere."

The old man put on his glasses, rummaged through some files in his desk, then brought out a sheet of paper at which he peered fondly.

"I don't say that this hand was the most sensational I've played," he said, "but I'd find it hard to think of a hand which gave me more lasting satisfaction. Now, this was in the early days. We were all trying to break away from Culbertson, but we didn't know in which direction to go. There was a lot of experimenting going on, trying out new ideas, especially in bidding. Still going on today, I guess, but there was something of the pioneer spirit about those early efforts of ours.

"Jim, I'm rambling. Let me get back to this hand. It came up in a grudge match. Remember Johnny Fanlow? Of course you do. He and I were partners for about three years until he took ill and died. Johnny and I were always crossing swords with the guys on the Jokers team—you never hear of them these days, but they were thought to be pretty hot stuff in the thirties. Anyway, we put up a challenge. Team of four match, one thousand dollars a man, winners take all. That was real money in those days, young man."

He looked at the sheet of paper again.

"Johnny and I got ourselves a pair of reliable teammates, and the whole bunch of us met at the old Parnassus Hotel. Not too many spectators, but the press corps was out in force, and there was a whole lot of tension. We needed to win that match, Jim. It wasn't the money so much, it was more like survival. Our self-esteem was at stake. Prestige. Call it what you like. And we had this feeling that the winners would be headed for the big-time and the others would be left on the dust-heap. And that's exactly the way it turned out.

"Well, they gave us a hell of a time. They were good, tough players. Or they were until this hand came along. This is the one that swung the match. See?"

This is what Jim Mantini saw on the faded yellowing sheet of paper held in the gnarled but steady fingers.

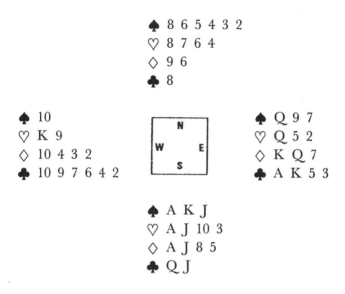

♠ 8 6 5 4 3 2
♡ 8 7 6 4
◇ 9 6
♣ 8

♠ 10
♡ K 9
◇ 10 4 3 2
♣ 10 9 7 6 4 2

♠ Q 9 7
♡ Q 5 2
◇ K Q 7
♣ A K 5 3

♠ A K J
♡ A J 10 3
◇ A J 8 5
♣ Q J

"Let me tell you first what happened to our other pair. They were East-West. It was game-all and East was the dealer. Our East player opened 1 No Trump—well, wouldn't you? South took a long look at his 21 points, decided they couldn't make it, and doubled. Our man in the West seat agreed with him, and took it out to 2 Clubs. North passed. East, who must have had a good sense of competitive psychology for those rather crude times, raised to 3 Clubs, which of course he had no right to do. And South doubled. I found out afterwards that he didn't just say the word 'Double'; he yelled it, and the saliva had already started trickling from the corners of his mouth. Disgusting. Well, they all passed. Now, let me see, what happened after that?"

Isaac consulted his sheet of notes again.

"Ah, yes. North led the 8 of Hearts; low card from dummy, the 10 from South, West won with the King. Then he pulled two rounds of trumps and led the King of Diamonds. That put South on the spot. He was good enough to play low, so he avoided giving away the overtrick, but there was no way he could touch the contract. You can imagine how our boys felt at the time, being doubled into game with cards like that.

"When the board came into our room, I was South, but this time East opened 1 Club instead of 1 No Trump. Don't ask me why; I never did find out. Well, about this time, we were fooling around with the direct overcall of the opponent's suit; we hadn't got our ideas properly straightened out, but we just used it as a super-strong bid. Not game-forcing, not even showing any special controls. So I bid 2 Clubs as a wait-and-see move.

"West did his duty, and bid 3 Clubs, which came round to me. I confess I didn't like the way things looked. According to the way the bidding had gone, North had to have at the most one Jack, but on the other hand, he also had to have no more than two Clubs, and quite possibly a singleton. So he had some length, and it was my problem to drill in the right spot to strike oil. I've often wondered just why I decided to bid Spades first, but I can't honestly remember now. You could put it down to sheer inspiration if you like. But the fact is that I bid 3 Spades, and Johnny Fanlow gave me 4.

"East doubled, and I had to give it a bit more thought. In the end I made up my mind I'd see it through. You could trust Johnny; beautiful judgment he had. West led the 10 of Clubs, and everybody looked at dummy for a long time. I guess they were all busy with their own thoughts, but you can imagine what mine were. Six trumps and a singleton. Who cares about points! I had more than half the points in the pack, and what I needed was shape, and that's what Johnny had given me.

"As you can see, there wasn't much to making the contract. I suppose you can see that, can't you, young man?"

Jim, whose bridge had never got out of the living-room, shook his head.

"OK. Let me explain. East took the Ace of Clubs and sent back the 2 of Hearts. I played the 10, and lost to West's King. Maybe the poor guy thought he was about to make his singleton trump, because he returned the 9 of Hearts in a hurry. I won with the Jack, ruffed a Club in dummy, then took the trump finesse against East's Queen. Two more rounds of trumps, then the Ace of Hearts, which brought down East's Queen. As you can see, I could then get over to dummy by playing the 3 of Hearts to the 8. After that, I led a Diamond, and East split his honors to avoid the overtrick. I lost just a Club, a Heart and a Diamond. So we finished up by making 3 Clubs doubled in one room and 4 Spades doubled in the other. That swung the match out of sight. I put $1,000 in my pocket, the press went crazy, and I got enough notoriety out of that one hand to get me into the international trials that year. After that, I never looked back."

Isaac put the paper away in his file, and carefully stowed the file in his desk. He turned sad and ruminative eyes on Jim.

"You don't see players like Johnny Fanlow today," he said softly. "The really great players I've met have generally been just one half of a great pair. You have to understand one other talented bridge player, and understand him as a human being, right down to his marrow. That's how Johnny and I were. That's probably why I picked out that hand to show you. It reminded me of how close we were."

For a minute or so, he gazed at the desk. Then he turned quickly back to Jim, and his eyes held a gleam.

"Mind you," he said, "that hand would set the cat among the pigeons just about anywhere and just about any time. The Jokers called it something quite uncomplimentary. I guess you young fellers would call it a fun hand."

Arbitration by Goofometer

When you thought of Ken, you thought of Harry. They were almost inseparable. They had been business partners for years, and the business had steadily prospered. In the tennis club's doubles tournaments, they were never far from making the final; one year, they had actually won, and their triumph was hailed as a victory for partnership understanding over mere technique. They took it in turns to crew for one another in the annual regatta, and their alternate displays of leadership and discipline were the envy of their fellow-sailors. But at bridge . . .

What is it about bridge that brings out the worst in people so often, and so seldom the best? Neither Ken nor Harry knew, but as neither of them was inclined to analysis, they dismissed the thought whenever it came up. But to the amusement of their friends they would fight like alley cats when a hand gave them a bad result, though the exchanges never soured to rancor and their tempers never got overheated.

One evening, at the house of their friends, Alan and Joyce Carrington, they started on a friendly rubber. It was not long before the sparks flew when Ken landed Harry in an absurd contract, got doubled, and lost 900. Alan and Joyce sat back and grinned until the flow of salty abuse eased off, then Joyce said: "If this goes on, we'll have to ask our guest to step in and arbitrate."

"I'll do my own arbitrating on this character," said Harry, then added, "What guest?"

Joyce announced, rather than merely stated, that one of the most celebrated names in the world of bridge was staying with them as house guest. He no longer took an active part in competitive bridge, she said, but his interest in the game was undimmed. He'd just gone into town to replenish his stock of tobacco; he wouldn't be long. And as she spoke, they heard the front door close, and in walked an elderly, amiable-looking man who smiled at them and waved his hand in greeting.

"You get on with your game," he said after the introductions were over. "I'm quite happy watching."

A couple of straightforward hands went by without incident. Then this was dealt by Harry with the score at game-all:

JOYCE
♠ 8 5
♡ K 10 9 6 4 3
♢ 10 4 3 2
♣ 5

KEN
♠ Q 10 9
♡ 2
♢ Q 8 7 6
♣ K Q 10 7 6

```
     N
 W       E
     S
```

HARRY
♠ 3
♡ A Q J 8 7 5
♢ A J
♣ A 8 4 2

ALAN
♠ A K J 7 6 4 2
♡ none
♢ K 9 5
♣ J 9 3

And this is how they bid it:

E	S	W	N
1 ♡	1 ♠	2 ♣	pass
3 ♡	3 ♠	dble	all pass

Ken led the King of Clubs, and trick by trick the play went:
1. The King of Clubs won, Harry playing the 8.
2. 2 of Hearts, 9, J and ruff by Alan.
3. Club ruff in dummy.
4. Diamond from dummy, Ace from Harry, Ken playing the 8.
5. Jack of Diamonds to Alan's King.
6. Club ruff in dummy.
7. Heart from dummy, covered, ruffed and over-ruffed.
8. Queen of Diamonds.
9. Diamond to dummy's 10, ruffed and over-ruffed.

Alan then drew trumps and claimed, "3 Spades doubled and made," he said happily. "That's game and rubber."

And that was the last uninterrupted remark made by anyone in the room for the next five minutes. Ken and Harry went into their act with unusual gusto, both doing their best to load the blame onto the shoulders of the other. Alan and Joyce made an occasional attempt to placate them, but grinned and gave it up until the storm had blown itself out. And as this anatomy of a catastrophe had been conducted with less than scientific objectivity, it got nowhere.

While the noisy fracas was going on, the guest was busy scribbling some notes, and when eventually the fury had abated, he came to the table and said:

"I guess what chiefly concerns you both at the moment is who's to blame for that little disaster. Right?"

"Right," said Ken and Harry in unison.

"Well," said the guest, "there are ways of determining such things, if you're both patient, if you can put up with an old-timer like me for a few moments. What I suggest is that we take a calm look at the bidding and the play, and see what we can learn from it. On the way, we'll use a goof scale to point up the errors. Let's say we award 8 points for a major error down to 1 or 2 points for a quite excusable lapse. When we're through, we'll know who chucked how much. Does that sound fair?"

Ken and Harry, quiet now, nodded.

"The bidding first, then. After 1 Heart from Harry and 1 Spade from Alan, Ken bids 2 Clubs. I'm not going to argue too strenuously against that bid, but a Negative Double, or a pass, might have been not only more appropriate, but more effective as things were. Ken gets 2 points on my scale for that—it's not all that serious. But now, Harry, that 3 Heart bid of yours was not well judged. I don't think your Hearts are quite good enough, and more important, your Clubs are much too good. So I'm going to make the running score: Harry 6; Ken 2.

"Now, your double of 3 Spades, Ken. Are you sure that isn't just a little bit trigger-happy? Sure you have 9 points, and you have a shortage in partner's suit; but you can't have it both ways—you can't ruff or over-ruff Heart leads and make trumps as well. I don't suppose it'll make you feel any better if I tell you that a sporting 3 NT from you would turn out to be unbeatable. Not that I honestly recommend it. But a pass would be far more circumspect. After all, if they make 3 Spades, you'll still be there on the next hand with a chance to clinch the rubber. But when you double, you place too many of your eggs in a rather fragile basket. So we get Harry 6; Ken 8.

"The final item in the bidding is Harry's decision to leave the double in. As a general rule, I have always tried to respect my partner's penalty doubles, but I think we all ought to leave enough freedom of action to pull the double when it seems that it's going to punish us, rather than our opponents. And in this case, Harry, you did mislead Ken about your Club holding. If you pulled the double and went out to 4 Clubs it would have been more than discreet, it would have been profitable. So the score goes to Harry 12; Ken 8.

"Now, to complete the audit, we'll take a quick look at the defence to 3 Spades doubled as it actually went. The Club lead is scarcely an error, though your signal with the 8 was pointless, Harry, unless you intended it as a suit-preference signal, in which case we won't argue."

Harry started to say something, changed his mind, and glared at Ken, who grinned cheerfully.

"But now, Harry, you were gravely at fault in not overtaking with your Ace to push a trump through. You should be able to guess that it would be difficult or even impossible for Ken to switch to a trump from his side without giving away a vital trick. It was your job to help him out, especially having seen dummy's single Club. So the score becomes Harry 20; Ken 8.

"When your King of Clubs held, Ken, I'm sure it was obvious to you that the prime need was to get partner in so that he could lead a trump. But the Heart lead wasn't much good for that purpose. You can place Harry with 6 Hearts for his jump rebid, dummy has 6 and you have one. Alan is marked with a void. A Diamond would have been much more to the point. That brings the score to Harry 20; Ken 14.

"When Alan led dummy's Diamond, Harry was right to go up with the Ace. But that 8 from you, Ken, was not only irrelevant, it was downright misleading, as I'm sure Harry will tell you in his own benevolent way. He thought you had the King, and that he'd be able to use his trump to ruff the third round. So we charge you another 6 for that, which brings the goof reading to 20–20. That wraps it up. Both very much to blame, but neither of you any more than the other."

He looked at Ken and Harry. Alan and Joyce looked at Ken and Harry. Ken looked at Harry while Harry looked at Ken. Then they all looked at the guest. Ken was the first to speak.

"I just thought of three or four smart things to say, but I don't think I'm going to say any of them. Right now I'm feeling too dumb to get smart. But I'll tell you one thing: for the first time in a long time, I've learnt something about myself from somebody else. Thanks for the lesson. You should have been in the Diplomatic Corps."

"I was," said the guest happily, "until I let myself get hooked by this little pastime of ours."

This Little Piggy Went to Market

One evening Sandy Melksham found that the cut had given him Don Foad as his left-hand opponent. Sandy had been there before with Don, and as Don's partner he had lost more money than he liked to think about through Don's obstinacy. Normally, Don was a fairly competent performer, but once he had a good hand, it was practically impossible for him to shake free of his original valuation of it.

The very first hand of the rubber was:

♠ K Q 8 7
♡ A Q 10 7
♢ J 5 2
♣ J 10

DON
♠ A 5 3
♡ K J 9 8 5
♢ A Q 4
♣ K Q

♠ 9 2
♡ 6 3
♢ K 10 8 3
♣ A 9 8 3 2

SANDY
♠ J 10 6 4
♡ 4 2
♢ 9 7 6
♣ 7 6 5 4

Sandy Melksham thought back to when he was a small boy living in the country. He grew familiar with many sayings of his farming friends. One of these was: "The quickest way to get a pig to market is to pull him by the tail in the opposite direction."

When Sandy left home and moved to the big city as a young man, determined to make his way in the world, he found that it was not only pigs that possessed this unreasonable but exploitable obstinacy. In his business dealings he was often able to apply the mechanics of counter-suggestion to good and profitable effect. And he found now, somewhat to his surprise, that at the bridge table many of his friends were similarly suggestible.

North was the dealer, and while the other players were still sorting their cards, Don said to North, "Your call," a sure sign that he himself had been dealt a good hand.

North bid 1 Spade, East passed, and Sandy, knowing that whatever he did was going to be ignored anyway, put in a whimsical 2 Spades.

Don frowned, grunted, and counted his points again. Still 19. What to bid? It never occurred to him for a fraction of a second to consider passing. He rejected 3 Hearts and 2 NT as underbids and settled for a take-out double.

North passed, and East, after a renewed inspection of his resources, bid 3 Clubs. Sandy, taking just slightly less time than he would normally take in a competitive situation, produced a crisp double.

Don grunted again. How could he let his partner massacre a 19-point hand by playing in a contract with only two trumps? Obviously he couldn't. One way or the other, this was destined to be a Heart hand, and a good one at that.

"Three Hearts," he said.

North fought back his jungle instincts. It was crystal clear that Don had a big hand. It seemed equally clear that he was due to go down in 3 Hearts. But was the double worth the risk? North felt reasonably sure of three trump tricks, and maybe a Spade, but what else? Besides, North mused, if I double, and Don runs to 3 NT, I can't guarantee to beat him on my own. If he goes down in 3 Hearts, so much the better; if he makes it, I'll be glad I didn't double. And North passed.

The others passed, East after long and puzzled thought, Sandy quickly and with relief.

The King of Spades was led, and allowed to hold. The Club shift was taken by the Queen, and the King was cashed. Then came the Ace of Spades and a Spade ruffed in dummy, after which a trump was led to Don's 8 and North's 10. North got off lead with the Queen of Spades, ruffed by Don, who then banged out the King of trumps.

North, winning with the Ace, led a Diamond to the Ace, and the Jack of trumps forced the Queen. After that, the hand played like a pianola, and Don made his contract, losing just 3 trumps and a Spade.

Don Foad was a great talker. He immediately launched into a breezy lecture on the accuracy of his judgment in the bidding, explaining at great length his reasons for doing this or for not doing that, and taking care to stress that events had vindicated him. All the others wanted to say something, but Don gave them no choice. North wanted to know where the hell Sandy got his two bids from. East wanted to know whether Don realized that 3 Clubs doubled would have been a pushover. Sandy would have liked his partner to know that his antics had probably kept Don out of a makeable 3 NT. But at the end of his peroration, Don swept the cards into a neat pile and started shuffling them.

"Your deal," he said to East.

Later in the same rubber, when it was game-all, Don dealt the following hand:

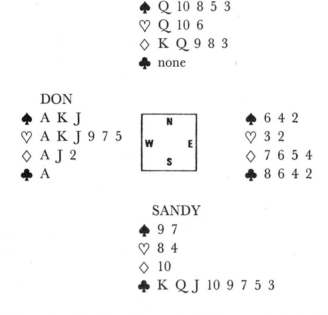

♠ Q 10 8 5 3
♡ Q 10 6
◇ K Q 9 8 3
♣ none

DON
♠ A K J
♡ A K J 9 7 5
◇ A J 2
♣ A

♠ 6 4 2
♡ 3 2
◇ 7 6 5 4
♣ 8 6 4 2

SANDY
♠ 9 7
♡ 8 4
◇ 10
♣ K Q J 10 9 7 5 3

When he picked up his cards, Don's eyes bulged. Quickly he counted. 25 points! Game at least, quite possibly a slam. He used the game-forcing bid of 2 Clubs to fire the first shot.

North could see that a reasonable sacrifice might be in the works if he found a fit in Sandy's hand, so he doubled, much to the relief of East, who found a pass easier to make than a conventional 2 Diamonds. Sandy really ought to have bid; he knew he should have said 4, or even 5, Clubs, but in the hope that Don got confused and passed, he converted North's double into a penalty double by passing.

Don was not in the least confused, but he was a bit excited. For the moment he contented himself by announcing a Heart suit by bidding a quiet 2 Hearts. Let them bid all the Clubs they wanted to. He still had 25 points.

After a pass from North, East now panicked; he had been hoping against hope that one of the opponents would buy the contract, but now that it had come around to him, he broke all the rules and passed, prepared to put up with his partner's . wrath rather than pay for his own rectitude.

Sandy knew that Don, given the chance, would bid on. He decided to stir the water with a bid of 3 Clubs. Don indeed did bid on. With an indignant glare at East he bid 3 Hearts, which not only North passed, but also East again. Conventions or no, he had gone on strike for the remainder of that auction.

Sandy thought of his partner's take-out double; he thought of East's strange refusal to bid anything even in an all-out forcing situation; he thought of the first hand of the rubber, when Don had triumphed so noisily over Sandy's stratagems; and he thought of the farmer in his old home town. Then he bid 4 Clubs.

Don's 4 Hearts was immediate and implacable. North's double was more to head off any further Club bids from Sandy than with the serious prospect of hurting 4 Hearts. Don's redouble was more in pity than in rage.

The King of Diamonds was led, and East, feeling like an outcast beggar at a feast of princes, put his dummy on display.

At that moment, Don had the contract in his grasp, but he got clever. North has no Clubs, he told himself, or he would surely have led one in view of Sandy's repeated Club bids. So any switch would help. A Spade would mean no losers in the suit, a trump would solve that problem, while if North didn't switch but continued Diamonds, he would make the Ace and the Jack. Don ducked, thereby sending his redoubled contract to the scaffold.

North led another Diamond. Sandy ruffed and led a Club. Don's Ace had its head laid on the block, to be briskly executed a second later by a trump from North. A third Diamond brought another axe down, and the Ace of Diamonds was laid low. Now another Club forced Don to ruff high, thereby promoting a trump trick for North. And there was still a Spade to lose. Down 3 redoubled. Minus 1600.

After Don had blustered and fumed himself into a petulant mumbling, North helpfully pointed out that if Don had taken the first Diamond lead, then played three rounds of trumps, the contract would have been on ice. North next turned his attention to Sandy.

"If they double 4 Clubs," he said, "we have nowhere to go. I hope you knew where we were supposed to be going when you bid it."

"The opposite way to the market," said Sandy.

The Carpet Coup

To start with, not even the street existed in the way that other streets do. And the mouldering building that housed the bridge club seemed to lie perpetually in the shadowy zone which separates reality from fantasy. The street was only a few yards long, one end being blocked by a crumbling wall. The house lay almost completely hidden from view behind spreading cedar trees with black and sinister branches. A few paces down the weed-strewn drive led you to a faded doorway flanked by tall windows with dusty and tattered lace curtains.

The bridge club occupied the main downstairs room. The members usually met after dark, where they were not quite so incongruous. By day, they appeared as shambling Hogarthian grotesques: snarling military men who had never forgiven the great powers for ending the war; vague elderly ladies, clutching the last remnants of a decaying gentility; pale retired professional men, who looked permanently guilty; bibulous travelling salesmen who always told the same stories; stockbrokers and insurance agents who had long since forgotten their reason for living; and Mr. Mezek.

At night, when the eerie greenish lampshades threw the same unworldly pallor over every face, and the corners of the room held clustered and menacing shadows, the club members somehow seemed to blend more naturally with their surroundings. Darkness made them kin.

They all knew one another well, and the relationships had

109

long ago crystallized beyond mutation, so that envy, hatred, fear, malice and vindictiveness stalked the room, palpable to an onlooker, but borne with indifference by all save Mr. Mezek. He loathed the atmosphere almost as much as he loathed the other members, but he knew how poor a player he was, and doubted whether any other club would accept him. Here, at least, he could play bridge, even though it was frequently an ordeal.

It was Friday the 13th, and Mr. Mezek was having a bad evening. He had made every mistake in the book, and had invented a few that nobody had ever seen before. His present partner, Mr. Brody, an over-large man with veined cheeks and an expression of permanent indignation, had almost run out of derisive remarks. In a querulous voice he demanded that Mr. Mezek "keep his eye on the ball."

Their opponents, Mr. and Mrs. Goyle, took more pleasure in defeating Mr. Mezek's contracts than they took in making their own. It was one of the reasons they came to the club so often. Mr. Goyle sneered and cackled all the time; his wife constantly whispered to herself, and occasionally burst out in subdued little sniggers.

Mr. Mezek bore all this with his usual humility. After all, it was still bridge, and what else was there to do? And one of these days he'd show them, though he didn't know how. He was kept going by the thought that one day he would pull off some triumph so rare and glittering that instant respect would come his way.

He dealt. His hands were trembling slightly and his glasses were misting over. He finished the deal and tried to sort his cards, but found he couldn't see them properly, so he put them on the edge of the table and wiped his lenses.

Unnoticed by anyone, the 5 of Diamonds fell to the floor. The deal—consisting at that moment of 51 cards—was:

MR. BRODY
♠ Q 4 3 2
♡ 6 5 4 3 2
◇ none
♣ A Q 6 5

MR. GOYLE
♠ 10 7 5
♡ Q J 9 8 7
◇ 3 2
♣ 10 8 7

MRS. GOYLE
♠ K 9 8 6
♡ A
◇ J 6 4
♣ K J 9 4 3

MR. MEZEK
♠ A J
♡ K 10
◇ A K Q 10 9 8 7
♣ 2

"Two Diamonds," said Mr. Mezek, flushing self-consciously. "Two No Trump," said Mr. Brody suspiciously. "Four Diamonds," said Mr. Mezek hesitantly. "Four Hearts," said Mr. Brody indignantly. "Six Diamonds," persisted Mr. Mezek defiantly. "Double," hissed Mrs. Goyle when it came around to her, and there was no more bidding.

Mr. Goyle, leering at Mr. Mezek, put the Queen of Hearts on the table, and Mr. Brody slammed down the dummy, disgust showing in every line of his face, which had gone mauve under the lights. The Goyles grinned after inspecting the dummy; old Mezek was going to pay out again.

Mrs. Goyle took the trick with her Ace, then for want of anything better, led a small Spade. Mr. Mezek fleetingly considered letting it run, but the sight of the menacing scorn on his partner's face deterred him. He would hold back the floodgates of anger as long as he could. Mournfully he played his Ace. Mrs. Goyle licked her lips and snickered something inaudible.

Then Mr. Mezek started down the only path he could see. He played out all his trumps. When the last one had gone, he played his King of Hearts. That left:

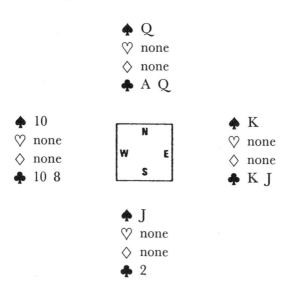

♠ Q
♥ none
♦ none
♣ A Q

♠ 10
♥ none
♦ none
♣ 10 8

♠ K
♥ none
♦ none
♣ K J

♠ J
♥ none
♦ none
♣ 2

Mr. Mezek, convinced that all depended on the Club finesse, and convinced also that it was doomed to fail, suddenly realized that even if it were to succeed, the Queen of Spades was still a loser. Strange. There was something funny somewhere. He looked again at dummy, then he looked at his own cards. He had 2 cards and dummy had 3! He stole a quick glance at the Goyles; they both had 3 cards. This fresh complication threw him into confusion and despondency. He hung his head.

And as he stared gloomily downwards, the pattern of the old worn carpet came into focus, and there appeared on it the unmistakeable shape of a playing card. It was the 5 of Diamonds. Mr. Mezek supposed it must be his. Somehow he must get it back into his hand before the others noticed anything wrong. Under the pretence of scratching his ankle, he retrieved the card, and a second or so later placed it on the table.

Mr. Goyle, with a shrug, played a Club. Mr. Mezek, obsessed with the inevitability of the Club finesse, played dummy's Queen of Spades. It was then Mrs. Goyle's turn to play, but for some reason she didn't seem to want to. She whispered furiously to herself, she shot venomous glances at Mr. Mezek, she looked despairingly at her husband for help, but none came. "This is most tiresome," she hissed to nobody in particular. And then, after drawing out one card and replacing it, then drawing out another only to put it back just as quickly, she suddenly grabbed her King of Spades and flung it onto the table.

After that, not even Mr. Mezek could go wrong.

Waiting for Gorrow

The ferryboat trip from the mainland took only about 30 minutes, but on an overcast, drab, bleak winter's day, that 30 minutes could stretch out interminably. As the ferry sputtered into motion, there was only the squalid array of wharves and warehouses to look at on one side, or the dismal grey water on the other. The Island wouldn't come into view for at least fifteen minutes. I went below, heading for the austere and barely-furnished little room I had seen before, which was euphemistically referred to as the Smoking Lounge. There might be a magazine in there. Maybe even a book.

As I swung back the heavy metal door and stepped over the threshold, I stopped suddenly. Three elderly people, two men and a woman, were sitting round a table in the middle of the room, a deck of cards spread out as though ready for the cut. None of them moved or even looked towards me. Nor did they seem to be looking at one another. They remained as immobile as frozen dinosaurs.

I took a closer look at the tableau. One man was small and fat; his legs were clad in leather gaiters; his obviously pensionable tweed suit had leather patches here and there; his face was pendulous and florid. A farmer from the Island, I thought. The woman sitting opposite the empty chair—and thus facing me—appeared to be every bit of 80, but her eyes, set deep among the mass of pallid wrinkly skin, shone with contrasting liveliness. The second man was tall and lean and

114

sad-looking; gray suit, gray tie, gray hair. Gray life too, I thought.

I closed the door softly behind me and took a seat on a battered old settee by the wall. The boat rocked slightly as she edged through the narrows. Nobody spoke. I picked up a three-year-old copy of "The Electrician." This is going to be an exciting trip, I told myself.

After nearly ten minutes, the tall lean man spoke:

"I have the feeling he isn't aboard. He's never kept us waiting as long as this before."

The small fat man grunted, then said:

"Didn't see him on the dock. Did you?"

Nobody answered that, and they all relapsed into silence.

Another five minutes went by. I felt I had absorbed all the hidden poetry and erotica of "The Electrician," so I went outside, cleared the smudged glass of a porthole with my sleeve, and peered through. Beyond the mist, the cliffs of the Island were faintly visible. Another 10 minutes or so to wait. I went back in again.

Still nobody had moved. Perhaps nobody could move. I wondered whether they would respond to a strange voice, so, looking at the cards, I asked:

"Ready for whist?"

"Bridge, young man." This was the woman. "Whist went out the year my husband died."

"I like bridge," I said, marvelling at my own temerity. "I've been playing for a couple of years. Would you care for me to sit in? We've got time for one hand before we get to the Island."

The tall lean man pointed to the empty chair, and said:

"Why, yes. You should have let us know before. We usually have a round of Chicago on the trip; both ways, you know. But our fourth seems to have stayed on the mainland. He's Mr. Gorrow, the undertaker. Perhaps you know him?"

I didn't know him, but I thanked them, pulled up my chair facing the old lady, and we cut for deal. I cut the Ace of Spades, which made them all wince slightly, and as I was dealing, I said to my partner, thinking of systems:

"What do you like to play?"

"Bridge," she said.

So much for systems. But as I was about to discover, the one and only deal just coming up was going to be memorable enough, without the added complication of systems.

"Suppose we make it game-all, since there's only going to be time for this one hand," I suggested. They agreed. I said nothing about stakes, and nobody else brought up the matter. I assumed we were just passing the time.

Here are the four hands as I dealt them from the South position:

(See next page)

The first round of bidding was a little bewildering: everybody bid my suit. It started like this:

S	W	N	E
1 ♣	2 ♣	3 ♣	4 ♣

My own bid seemed to me to be eminently conservative, reasonable, unostentatious; orthodox beyond reproach. I could hear a bell clanging in the engine-rooom. There was no time for lengthy interrogations. I took a quick glance at my partner, an aged Sarah Battle. She had closed her cards with majestic finality, and had clearly washed her hands of the whole affair. Before deciding what to do next, I gave some thought to the 2 Club bid. It occurred to me afterwards that

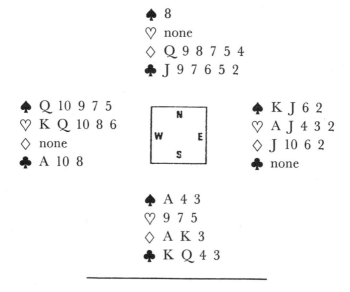

♠ 8
♡ none
◇ Q 9 8 7 5 4
♣ J 9 7 6 5 2

♠ Q 10 9 7 5
♡ K Q 10 8 6
◇ none
♣ A 10 8

♠ K J 6 2
♡ A J 4 3 2
◇ J 10 6 2
♣ none

♠ A 4 3
♡ 9 7 5
◇ A K 3
♣ K Q 4 3

the fat man on my left had heard of the direct 2 ♣ overcall which was at that time enjoying a short vogue. It showed limited strength, but offered a fit in either of the major suits. The thin man had confirmed his major suit holdings, and his willingness to let his partner choose, by his bid of 4 Clubs.

At the time, these subtleties were wasted on me. I just thought they were all having a joke at my expense, and the joke had gone quite far enough. I doubled. West passed, and the spotlight swung round to my partner. She hissed her "Pass" through clenched dentures. The one bright feature of her appearance was the faded red velvet hat she wore, which sported an enormous feather. After making her pass, she nodded at East like the figure of doom, so that the red feather dipped menacingly towards him.

He remained remarkably calm. Not only that. He redoubled, and the feather jerked upright in astonished indignation. I passed, feeling totally lost. West now bid 4 Hearts, presumably allowing leeway for his partner to exercise his discretion and go to 4 Spades if that appeared to be the better spot.

North's feather was now ominously still. The old lady had closed her eyes, and I thought for a few moments that she was showing her supreme contempt for the proceedings by taking a little nap. But a silent revolution was taking place under that red hat and behind those wrinkled lids. A quarter of a century's unflinching devotion to the point count was being called into question. She began to have the feeling that the key to this bothersome auction lay in her own cards. Partner had bid Clubs: she had 6 of them. Partner had not bid any other suit: he could ruff his losers until doomsday with her trumps. Partner would surely have at least one big Diamond: he would have extra tricks growing up all over the place. Her hand got better and better the more she thought about it.

She took one last look at her hand and tried to dismiss the notion of "3 points." Then, resolutely, she moved into the new era. Opening her eyes, and fixing me with an occult stare, she said:

"I bid 6 Clubs."

East doubled. I don't blame him. I might have done the same myself. But when West led the King of Hearts and the old lady, feather bobbing busily, arranged her dummy for me to see, all other thoughts vanished, leaving only incredulous delight.

There was nothing to the play. I ruffed and led a trump. West won and returned a trump, and I drew his last trump with a third round. Then the Ace, King and Queen of Diamonds, a Diamond ruff, a Heart ruff, and the hand was over.

My venerable partner had apparently taken the success of the contract for granted from about half-way through the play. She was busy with her arithmetic. I saw columns of figures being totted up carefully.

"It's 1,540," I said, trying to be helpful.

She ignored me and addressed herself to East and West, who were looking sullen and rebellious.

"Whatever it is, it's a lot better than you deserve," she said sternly. "I've just worked out what you lads would have had to pay out in your 4 Clubs redoubled. Far as I can see, you only make the Ace of Clubs. That's 9 down, doubled and redoubled and vulnerable too. I make that 5,200."

And she suddenly burst out into loud cackles. East and West didn't see anything too humorous in the situation. They just looked dourly at each other. It occurred to me that if it did really happen the way the old lady figured it, it would surely be the most disastrous penalty in the history of bridge.

There was a grating and a bumping as the ferry pulled alongside the pier. Ropes squealed. Voices rang out.

I got up from the table, and took a last look at the trio. They had formed themselves into the same frozen tableau as when I first saw them. None of them spoke or moved or looked in my direction.

I left the door open and went up on deck, glad of the icy salt air on my face.

End of a Partnership

Joe and Myra Daley had been married for over thirty-five years, and had been bridge partners for most of that time. Myra was large, impassive, taciturn, except when her husband's lapses drove her to scorn, and then she was very eloquent indeed. She was in fact a very good player, and her ability might have carried her to the heights of the tournament world if it were not for just one defect—her husband.

Joe's game could at best be described as useful; as long as the hands fitted their system, he could be relied on to bid as accurately as the next player, and he could steer a tricky contract home as well as anyone. But he had a faulty memory, which now and again let him down with a sad thump.

For years, Joe and Myra yearned to take top prizes in a national competition, but they had never made it, though they had come close enough at times. Now they sat in the huge arena among hundreds of tables, tensely bidding and playing their way through the qualifying phase of the National Open Pairs. They made an odd sight together; Joe weighed a hundred and thirty pounds when he married, and had never lost or gained more than a pound or two, and next to Myra's huge bulk he seemed almost pathetically frail. He was mercurial, talkative, sociable; she was reticent and aloof. He looked around him constantly, like a bird at feed; she never moved, and for long moments looked like a figure carved in stone.

If they had really wanted to fulfil their bridge aspirations, they would have sought separate partners years ago, but a combination of habit and loyalty kept them together. Apart from Joe's weak memory, he was in dread of his wife's searing contempt for any mistake he might make, and this kept him in a perpetual state of nervous anxiety. As the qualifying round approached its half-way point, Joe pulled his cards out of the board and found that, as West, he was the dealer at game-all.

JOE		MYRA
♠ K 3		♠ A Q 6 4
♡ Q 9 4		♡ A 10 3 2
◇ A K 8 3		◇ 9 2
♣ J 10 4 2		♣ Q 7 3

Joe bid 1 NT; North passed; Myra said 2 Clubs. This was routine. They were playing the Weak No Trump throughout, with Stayman. While Myra could have gone straight to 3 NT on her cards, she knew that a fit in one of the majors might well result in their making a vital overtrick. So she bid 2 Clubs to find out whether Joe held 4 cards in either of the major suits.

But Joe, just at that moment, was distracted. The players at an adjoining table, instead of being engrossed silently in their game, were chatting and laughing with a tall young man who was standing by the side of the table with a large sheet of paper in his hand. As Joe watched, the man made a few notes on the paper, then moved over to the Daleys' table.

"Excuse the interruption, folks," he said, "we shall be bringing refreshments round in about an hour, and I'd like to take your orders now to save time."

He told them what was available, and invited them to make a selection. He was a very cheerful and polite young man, and he took a professional pride in knowing how to put people at their ease. Joe questioned him closely about what drinks could be ordered; their two opponents exchanged a few pleasantries with him; Myra sat immobile, quickly ordering cheese sandwiches and coffee, then attending to her cards again, as though reminding the rest of the table that there was serious work ahead of them, and that trifling with details like food was not something she could approve of.

The waiter departed. Joe, aware that his wife had made a bid immediately before the interruption, said: "What did you bid, partner?"

"Two Clubs," said Myra, with ill-disguised contempt.

Joe sat up straight and took another look at his hand. He had quite forgotten that he himself had opened 1 NT. They were playing a version of Acol, and an opening bid of 2 Clubs was the strongest of all openings. And here he was with 13 points yet!

Trying to control his racing pulse, he decided to bid this one scientifically; he would show the old battle-axe that he was quite capable of handling a situation like this. There must be a slam somewhere, maybe even a grand! Mastering a temptation to bid 3 NT to show a balanced hand with extra values, he bid 3 Diamonds.

Myra Daley slowly folded her cards together and fixed him with an intense and pitying stare. The old fool had lost his marbles. Here he is, opening with a weak no trump, and after a Stayman response he goes berserk and bids 3 Diamonds. But wait—she said to herself—was it just possible that his opening 1 NT was a tactical bid based on a long Diamond suit? They had used such a bid now and again with occasional success. And after all, he did take rather a long time to make up his mind what to bid. She would make a temporizing bid of 3 Hearts, and let him decide where to go from there.

There was no confusion in Joe's mind. His wife had a power-house of a hand with a good Heart suit. What to do now? If he raised the Hearts, she might pass, and he was far too good for that. How could he convey the information that he had 13 points? Bid 3 NT? No, he decided, she might pass that as well. He would just have to take control himself. Firmly he bid 4 NT.

Myra Daley raised her head very slowly, an inch at a time, her face a gorgon-like mask of withering scorn. It was incredible. After all these years she would have to look for a new partner. He opens a weak no trump, and without hearing a single forcing bid from his partner, starts looking for a slam. She concluded that he had quite suddenly entered his second childhood, right in the middle of an important tournament. But Blackwood was Blackwood, and her rigorous principles refused to let her do anything other than make the prescribed response. She bid 5 Hearts.

Joe was disappointed. A powerhouse with only two Aces; well he would have to be content with a small slam. He bid 6 Hearts. Myra sighed heavily and passed. Events were entirely beyond her comprehension. She started to accumulate a list of the things she intended to say to him once this bizarre episode was over. Then the Ace of Clubs was led, and Joe arranged his dummy, glowing with rectitude. She gasped. She blinked several times. She hissed a corrosive obscenity at him that made his thinning hair stand on end. She looked wildly around her, as though seeking witnesses to this mindless atrocity.

The Ace and King of Clubs were followed by a third Club which was ruffed. And she had to lose a trump trick. 3 down.

"What kind of 2 Club bid do you call that?" demanded Joe with a rare flash of courage.

Myra Daley forgot her mental list. The matter had gone past the point where words could make any difference. She picked up the board which had contained the hand they had just played, stood up so as to get better aim, and clouted him across the side of the head with it.

"You stupid old cow!" howled Joe, clutching his head.

With hundreds of eyes on them, they stalked out of the room, out of the tournament, out of their partnership. And they left by separate doors.

A Blood Match

They took their bridge seriously in Ormon Island. The standard wasn't all that hot, mind you, but the local enthusiasts fought tooth and nail for the annual teams title. There were just four little towns on the island, which made things convenient for the bridge organizers; each team held its own eliminations during the year, and the winning team from each town took part in the semi-finals, with the two surviving winning teams going into the final.

The veteran players from South Cove had reached the final once again, and when the party of five drove off to head for Grapes Bay, where the 48-board final was to be played, they had a warm send-off from their local supporters. In addition to the four members of the team, Ginger Egan went along as driver, scorer, messenger and odd-job boy.

Ginger was 19. He had been playing bridge for just over a year, and was thought by some people to have a bright future at the game, although he had yet to play in his first tournament. Now, as he sat at the wheel and started the motor, he turned his freckled face to the assembled well-wishers and bawled happily: "See you tomorrow night when we come back with the cup. And make sure you've got something interesting to put in it. We'll be thirsty after the drive home." And away they went.

Just after midday the following day the final began. It was a dour struggle right from the start, neither team yielding anything much, and the first session ended with the scores even.

When the second session began, both teams began to look for opportunities to create swings, but the hands were flat, and the only IMP's to be surrendered were as the result of overtricks or partials.

The tension mounted, Ginger as tense as anyone else. The Open Room was the hotel lounge, and a good crowd of spectators turned up to see the action. With just three boards to go, it was still wide open. 1 NT made with an overtrick. Nothing there. Then a hand passed out, and everybody gave a great groan of frustration. The last board was placed on the table.

Ginger, sitting just behind one of the South Cove players, saw him suddenly throw back his head and hastily tug a handkerchief from his pocket. Within seconds the handkerchief was soaked in blood. Ginger went forward quickly and helped the man to his feet, then led him towards the nearest settee, where he was gently laid down. The cards remained untouched in the board.

A few minutes later, a doctor arrived, examined the prostrate player, and announced that it was not all that serious, just a minor nasal hemorrhage. But he advised the man to remain lying down for at least an hour.

"An hour!" exclaimed his partner. "We've got to get home tonight. He can't play the last hand lying down."

The Grapes Bay pair were sympathetic, but had no suggestion to offer.

"Pity you didn't bring a reserve," said one of them.

Then everybody looked at Ginger.

"Does he play?" asked someone.

"Well—," started the South Cove player who had been rendered partnerless, but he was interrupted by Ginger himself.

"Of course I can play," he said, and he said it in such a way as to make the question seem superfluous. "Last board, right?"

They got formal assent from the Grapes Bay captain for this departure from text, then Ginger took his place at the table. The last board showed game-all, dealer South. The crowd of spectators drew closer to see how this unlikely reserve was going to perform now that the crisis had descended.

Unknown to anyone in the Open Room, the hand just about to be played had caused some heartburning in the Closed Room.

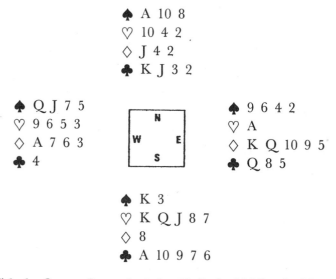

```
              ♠ A 10 8
              ♡ 10 4 2
              ◊ J 4 2
              ♣ K J 3 2

♠ Q J 7 5                      ♠ 9 6 4 2
♡ 9 6 5 3          N           ♡ A
◊ A 7 6 3      W       E       ◊ K Q 10 9 5
♣ 4                S           ♣ Q 8 5

              ♠ K 3
              ♡ K Q J 8 7
              ◊ 8
              ♣ A 10 9 7 6
```

With the Grapes Bay pair sitting N–S, the bidding had been:

S	W	N	E
1 ♡	pass	1 NT	2 ◊
2 ♡	pass	3 ♡	pass
4 ♡	pass	pass	pass

127

West had led the Ace of Diamonds and followed with a small Diamond to East's 10, ruffed by South, who now led the King of trumps to East's Ace. East forced South with another Diamond, and again South ruffed. South, now uneasy about losing trump control, went after his side-suit, taking a first-round finesse of the Jack of Clubs and losing to East's Queen. The canny East then returned a Club which West ruffed, and that was that. One down: 100 to E–W.

In the Open Room, with Ginger in the South seat, the bidding took a different course:

S	W	N	E
1 ♡	pass	1 NT	2 ◇
3 ♣	3 ◇	4 ♡	pass
6 ♡	pass	pass	pass

The North player, sensing that Ginger had got the bit between his teeth, and nervous about landing him in a high contract, had decided that the only way to head him off was to deposit him straight into game by jumping to 4 ♡. But Ginger, his eyes alight with visions of valor, ignoring the initial weak 1 NT response, and not even deigning to check for Aces via Blackwood, shot into slam.

West, on lead, was worried. He knew that when voids were about, players often bid a slam direct, as Blackwood would not tell them what they wanted to know. And what would be more natural on that bidding than for South to have a void in Diamonds. Give East 6 for his overcall, North 3 for his 1 NT response, and 4 in front of his nose, West could see that the Ace of Diamonds might hinder rather than help the defence. Partner surely had either the Ace or King of Spades, thought West; he led the Queen of Spades.

"Don't worry about the overtrick," said North with grim sarcasm as he put down his dummy.

But that was lost on Ginger, who had his armor on, his lance gripped tightly in one hand and his vizor being pulled down with the other. This was the real thing!

He called for a small Spade from dummy, and won the trick with his King. The 3 of Spades was led straight back, and dummy's 10 inserted. Now the Ace of Spades allowed Ginger to throw his Diamond. Next, a small trump went to East's Ace, and the Diamond return was ruffed, to the disgust of East. Ginger then drew trumps, played to the King of Clubs, ran the Jack successfully, came back to his Ace of Clubs, bringing down the Queen, and with his contract assured, insisted on playing out every card right down to the last, unwilling to give up the role of hero until he was forced to.

"Gee, I'm sorry there aren't any more hands," he said.

"Me too," said North with a profound relief that belied his words. "One or two more like that, and you'd really put South Cove on the world bridge map."

As the car drew into the South Cove town square late that night, a small throng of enthusiasts moved towards it eagerly. Ginger, his face pushed out of shape by a huge grin, brandished the cup as he got out of the car, and was greeted by loud cheers.

"You really socked it to them, then," said one supporter happily.

"Yes, sir," replied Ginger. "First we had a nose bleeder, but then we put them down for the count."

He looked around expectantly, waiting for someone to ask him how it all happened. He need not have worried. Years later, they're still asking him, and he's still glad to tell them.

Inferno Revisited

The stranger paid the cab driver, looked around him for a few moments, then consulted the back of an envelope which he drew from his pocket. Should be right across the street from here, he thought. And sure enough, as he gazed at the parade of lettered signs above the stores, he saw in discreet bronze capitals: KINGSVILLE BRIDGE CLUB.

He took a glance at his watch. A bit early. Well, time for a chat if anybody's there. Inside the Club, the main room was empty. There was a large notice-board in one corner, and the stranger strolled over. His attention was immediately riveted by the centerpiece, which was an ordinary travelling scoresheet, apparently used in a recent tournament. The hand which had accompanied this scoresheet on its rounds had obviously been far from ordinary, for there were rings around some of the scores, exclamation marks against others, heavy underlinings, and caustic comments scribbled in the margins.

His curiosity mounted. He peered more closely. About a dozen tables had been in play, and in every single case the declarer on that board had registered a minus score, in some cases quite a heavy one. He saw one or two redoubled contracts and a number of doubled ones. He also noticed that West, North and East had each been at the helm, but there was no mention of South.

A movement caught his eye. In a small adjoining office a man was sitting at a desk. The stranger walked over, knocked politely, and said: "Hello, there. I'm staying in town just for the night. Any chance of a game?"

"Sure thing. But you're a bit early. Say about another 40 minutes or so."

"I'll wait. Tell me, that scoresheet over there on your notice-board—that's a wild one, eh? Must have been quite a deal."

"You can say that again! Like to see it? I've got a record of it in the office. I make a habit of jotting down anything as weird as that."

At that moment, three men came in and joined in the conversation. The man in the office, who turned out to be the Club Secretary, produced a thick folder and started rummaging around inside it. He said: "This gentleman was just asking about that crazy hand in last week's duplicate. He wants to see the deal."

"He should," said one of the men. "Better still, he should play it. Why not? We've got plenty of time."

They sat down at a table, while the secretary sorted a deck of cards into an exact replica of the infamous deal.

"Let's put you South," said the secretary.

"Wait a minute," said the stranger. "I can't remember all the details of that scoresheet, but I do seem to remember that everyone except South came in for some heavy licks."

"We like to treat newcomers gently," said the secretary with a grin. "Here are your cards; it's game-all, and West is the dealer."

Unknown to the stranger, who of course could see only his own 13 cards, this was the deal:

(See next page)

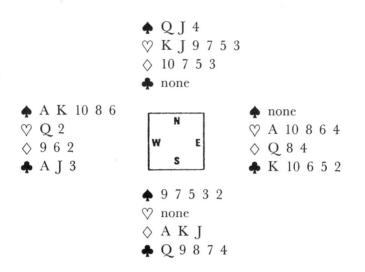

♠ Q J 4
♡ K J 9 7 5 3
◇ 10 7 5 3
♣ none

♠ A K 10 8 6
♡ Q 2
◇ 9 6 2
♣ A J 3

♠ none
♡ A 10 8 6 4
◇ Q 8 4
♣ K 10 6 5 2

♠ 9 7 5 3 2
♡ none
◇ A K J
♣ Q 9 8 7 4

"I had this hand last week," said West, "and I might as well tell you that I opened 1 Spade, so I'm going to do that again."

"Well, I didn't hold these cards," said North, "but I'll do what most Norths would do. I bid 2 Hearts."

"Double," said East without any preamble.

So it's one of those, thought South to himself. Partner has a weakish hand with a Heart suit. In Hearts, I'm going to be as much use to him as a leaky boat. What would he make of a redouble, I wonder. If I was sure he'd treat it as SOS, I'd redouble, and let him bid even a 3-card suit. It ought to be less expensive than 2 Hearts doubled. But suppose he leaves it in! Was there a redoubled Heart contract on that scoresheet? I can't remember now. Better forget the idea anyway; it might be a bit embarrassing to go down a couple of thousand on the first hand I play in the place. What about bidding Clubs? I ought to know better. If you take unilateral action in this kind of situation, you usually finish up by making things worse. Wait. There is one thing I could do, and that's bid Spades. On this bidding he can't imagine I'm strong; if he's got a second suit, he'll bid it; if he's got a Spade honor, he might get out lightly in No Trump; if it's got to be Hearts, well, it'll be just one more down and it can't be helped.

Having thus reasoned, the stranger bid 2 Spades.

West was clearly thrown out of his stride by this development. After nearly a minute he turned to the stranger and said: "You must bear in mind that I know the full hand. It's a little difficult for me to decide what I'd do if I were seeing my cards for the first time. Maybe I'd double. Come to think of it, that's what I'm gonna do right now. Double."

North passed. East, clearly unhappy, also passed. The stranger, realizing that a redouble here would be even greater folly than before, saw nothing for it but to bite on the bullet and pass. Which he did. And to his surprise, he found himself the focal point of three wide grins.

"My lead," said West. "I think I ought to trust my partner; I'll lead the Queen of Hearts, without malice aforethought."

The Queen of Hearts was covered by dummy's King and East's Ace, South ruffing. He ruffed a Club in dummy, then led a Diamond to his Jack. Then came the Ace and King of Diamonds, all following, much to South's relief. Another Club ruff in dummy allowed him to cash the Jack of Hearts. And South had taken the first 7 tricks.

He then played dummy's Queen of trumps, and no matter what West did, another trump trick had to go to South.

"The only South player to play the hand," said North.

"The only player in any seat to make a plus score," said West.

"The only player to keep his head," said East.

"Congratulations," said the secretary. "Hey, want a partner for tonight?"

Trick Psychist

It should be admitted straight away in favor of Brad Wilkinson that his tactics were surprisingly effective on more occasions than they had any right to be. The entire membership of the Club knew that his liking for the psychic bid amounted to addiction, and they were constantly on the alert for any funny business. Yet time after time it arrived, and time after time it paid off. Brad operated on the principle, which he didn't spread around too freely, that provided he varied both the type and range of the psyche, he was actually harder to stereotype than the flagrant overbidder or the notorious underbidder.

At the table he was smooth, slick and plausible, but as a high pressure salesman for the Lorelei Corporation he was that way all the time. His bridge was simply an extension of his working role. Success, to Brad, was inseparably linked with persuasion, and if persuasion occasionally involved a little deception, well, he could handle that too.

I was watching a rubber at the Club when a typical Brad coup was executed. The deal was:

(See next page)

At love-all, East dealt and passed. South opened 1 Diamond, and Brad, holding the West cards, said a cool 1 No Trump. North doubled, of course. East passed again, as did South. Now Brad bid a firm 2 Diamonds. North doubled again, and there were two more passes. Brad, a little less firmly, now bid 3 Clubs.

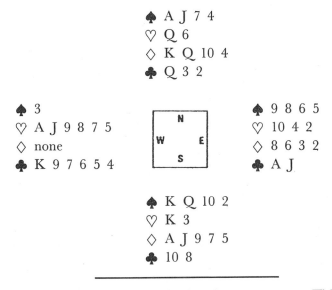

♠ A J 7 4
♡ Q 6
◇ K Q 10 4
♣ Q 3 2

♠ 3
♡ A J 9 8 7 5
◇ none
♣ K 9 7 6 5 4

♠ 9 8 6 5
♡ 10 4 2
◇ 8 6 3 2
♣ A J

♠ K Q 10 2
♡ K 3
◇ A J 9 7 5
♣ 10 8

Another double from North. Another two passes. This time, Brad paused for deliberation, which was all part of the act, but it would have happened in any case if he had been making genuine bids. His eventual 3 Hearts could be said to have been slightly on the subdued side. The regulation double followed, and East and South passed for the last time, one with resignation, the other jubilantly.

The jubilation soon wore off. After standing the double, Brad ruffed the opening Diamond lead and banged out the Ace and another trump. South's King of Spades took the next trick, South never guessing that it was the last one his side was going to make. Brad ruffed the Spade continuation, then finessed the Jack of Clubs. After the Ace had been cashed, he returned to his hand with a ruff, and it was time to claim. 3 Hearts doubled, with 2 overtricks.

North and South were still at each other's throats when I was called away to join in a rubber at another table.

On another occasion, I watched Brad perpetrate a different kind of psyche. Or a double-psyche, to be more accurate. These were the hands:

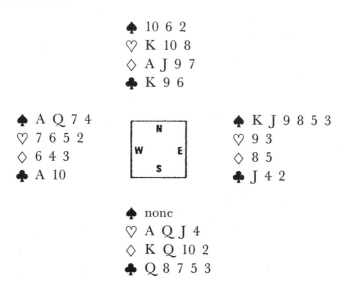

```
              ♠ 10 6 2
              ♡ K 10 8
              ◇ A J 9 7
              ♣ K 9 6

♠ A Q 7 4          N          ♠ K J 9 8 5 3
♡ 7 6 5 2     W        E      ♡ 9 3
◇ 6 4 3            S          ◇ 8 5
♣ A 10                        ♣ J 4 2

              ♠ none
              ♡ A Q J 4
              ◇ K Q 10 2
              ♣ Q 8 7 5 3
```

At game to North–South, North dealt and passed. East hesitated for just the tiniest moment, then also passed. To my amazement, I heard Brad, in the South seat, open 1 Spade. West, of course, had nothing to say, but North introduced a complication by jumping all the way to 3 No Trump. After a pass by East, Brad did one of his long thinks. You will no doubt agree that he had something to think about.

You will also agree that 3 NT would not be an overwhelming success. East was far more acquainted with Brad's methods than North was; East certainly would not have hesitated to lead a Spade against 3 NT. Moreover, Brad knew this, and after quite some little while, his second psyche emerged. He bid 4 No Trump.

Now at this particular club, quantitative raises of No Trump were virtually unknown. If you as much as touched the 4 NT button, the Blackwood machinery was activated automatically. North dutifully responded 5 Diamonds, and Brad passed!

North sat with an angry frown on his face until dummy appeared. As the tricks came rolling in without effort, the frown evaporated, and was replaced by a sunny smile. He didn't play the Clubs to the best effect, but he still wound up with eleven tricks.

Afterwards I said to Brad: "Very smart. But suppose your partner had turned up with 2 Aces and bid 5 Hearts. He'd never have been able to cope with the 4–2 split."

"Suppose my partner had 3 Aces, and bid 5 Spades," answered Brad. "Do you think I'd have left him to cope with *an opposing* 6–4 trump split? What's more, I had no guarantee that he held 4 Diamonds; for all I knew, Hearts might have been the best place for him. No, my original intention was to jump straight to 6 Clubs over whatever he responded. I get away with it, too. Small to the King, then run the 9 on the way back."

"What made you change your mind?"

"Vibes. When you bid the way I bid, you learn to trust the vibes. The vibes told me 5 Diamonds was cool, so I left it. If I'd got bad vibes, I'd have jumped to 6 Clubs. Of course," he added philosophically, "I might have been jumping into something even more messy than 3 NT."

Either the vibes only worked part time, or now and again they conspired to work against him, because there's no denying the fact that his tactics let him down with a resounding crash on occasion. One such occasion took place when I was at the table. I was sitting East, and Brad was the dealer at game-all in the South seat. Here are the hands:

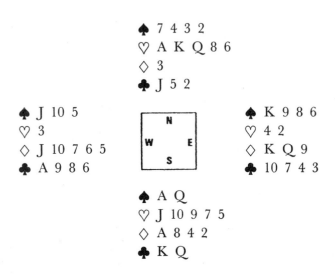

♠ 7 4 3 2
♡ A K Q 8 6
◇ 3
♣ J 5 2

♠ J 10 5
♡ 3
◇ J 10 7 6 5
♣ A 9 8 6

♠ K 9 8 6
♡ 4 2
◇ K Q 9
♣ 10 7 4 3

♠ A Q
♡ J 10 9 7 5
◇ A 8 4 2
♣ K Q

Normally, Brad would have eschewed the obvious, and instead would have bid 1 NT as being slightly trickier. But he listened to his vibes, and bid a perfectly orthodox 1 Heart. West passed, and so did North! I had no intention of interfering with the East cards, and Brad made an unbid small slam with the minimum of exertion and the maximum of frustration.

An interesting conversation then ensued, with North pointing out that only Brad's well-earned reputation stood between him and a good result.

"Once you bid a Heart, and I hold all the Hearts," began North, "naturally I think you've got another suit, probably Spades. I figure we can make 2 or 3 Spades, but why sweat when we can stay safely in 1 Heart?"

"So why not bid 1 Spade in that case?" asked Brad, exasperated by his partner's logic.

"On four to the 7-spot? Are you serious?"

"You don't usually pass your partner's opening bid when you've got 10 points, do you?"

"You don't usually have an opening bid when you make one, do you?"

There was no textbook answer to this question, which in any case was not a textbook question.

"What's more," added North, determined to have the last word, "I still haven't forgotten last Thursday."

Neither West nor I was at the Club on that Thursday, and we were both curious to know what had stung North so badly.

"Next deal," said Brad, who had had enough for the moment.

It was not until the end of that rubber that West and I were able to take North aside and get him to tell us Thursday's tale. It appeared that North was again in the North seat on that occasion, Brad was South, and they were non-vulnerable against vulnerable opponents. West had dealt the following hand:

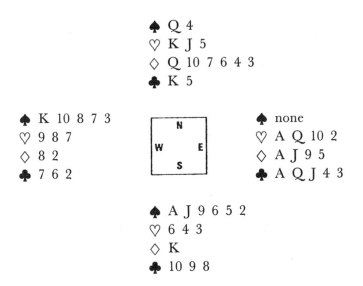

```
              ♠ Q 4
              ♡ K J 5
              ◇ Q 10 7 6 4 3
              ♣ K 5

♠ K 10 8 7 3      N        ♠ none
♡ 9 8 7                    ♡ A Q 10 2
◇ 8 2        W       E     ◇ A J 9 5
♣ 7 6 2           S        ♣ A Q J 4 3

              ♠ A J 9 6 5 2
              ♡ 6 4 3
              ◇ K
              ♣ 10 9 8
```

North, a conservative and somewhat nervous player, had

passed after West had started the auction with a pass; East had bid 1 Club, and Brad, almost predictably, had come in with 1 Diamond. After West's second pass, North, still ultra-conservative and more wary than ever, had contented himself with a simple raise to 2 Diamonds. For just a moment, they had the East-West pair over a barrel, but Brad had let them go free, and strapped himself there instead:

W	N	E	S
pass	pass	1 ♣	1 ◇
pass	2 ◇	pass	2 ♠
pass	pass	3 ◇(!)	pass
pass	dble	redble(!)	3 ♠
dble	pass	pass	pass

Brad had gone 4 down, and had then been forced to listen to a stern lecture from North on how this loss of 700 points could easily have been converted to a handsome gain if only he hadn't panicked into removing the redouble.

As this tale unfolded, we wondered whether the lessons had been absorbed by the wayward Brad. They had. Now Brad is the embodiment of rectitude when facing this particular North, but whenever he cuts him as an opponent, the whole battery of fanciful and irregular bidding armaments is turned in that direction. Maybe Brad knows that an angry bridge player is like an angry car driver: there is no way that cool judgment can operate with its usual effectiveness, and disasters pile up to prove it.

Heart in the Right Place

Old Doc Rubins never talked about himself very much; he lived alone on the outskirts of the small town, and nobody knew whether he was a doctor of medicine, philosophy, or what. He had moved in about five years ago, minded his own business, kept his own counsel, and apparently lived just for bridge.

In West Kelton, bridge was regarded as a social activity, and Doc was not noticeably sociable. He would arrive at the club, stare around at the members with an inscrutable gaze, nod briefly to anyone who greeted him, then wait to cut in. Once in, he gave his whole attention to the game, and would have little patience with attempts to exchange gossip or small talk. He would interrupt some promising item of local scandal by saying bluntly: "Your deal." And if anybody were to have the effrontery to ask him outright what he did for a living, he would snap: "Minin'."

"Minin'?"

"Yes. Minin' my own damn business."

This habit did not endear him to the West Kelton bridge club, but he was known to be a player of great depth and trickiness. He was welcomed as a partner and looked on with wary respect as an opponent.

His hair was grey and his face lined; his shoulders had a perpetual stoop. But there was nothing doting about his game, which was full of an almost youthful vigor and audacity. Like most loners, he was happiest when he was declarer, though now and then in defence I saw him pull off a coup which staggered the rest of the table and gave the kibitzers something to buzz about for days afterwards.

I remember vividly one such occasion. With North and South vulnerable, and Doc in the East seat, he held:

♠ 8 7
♡ J 3
◇ A K J 9 8 6 5
♣ A 4

North dealt, and opened 1 Heart. Doc's voice was quite steady as he came in with 4 Diamonds. A very long pause followed. Eventually, South bid 4 Spades, and everybody passed. West led the 7 of Diamonds, and I wandered round the table inspecting the hands. This is what I saw:

♠ A Q
♡ K Q 10 8 7 4
◇ 3
♣ K J 8 7

♠ 10 3 2   ♠ 8 7
♡ 6 5 2   ♡ J 3
◇ 7 4   ◇ A K J 9 8 6 5
♣ Q 10 9 6 2   ♣ A 4

```
        N
    W       E
        S
```

♠ K J 9 6 5 4
♡ A 9
◇ Q 10 2
♣ 5 3

Fortunately for Doc, South was spending quite a little while doing some inspecting of his own before playing to the first trick, which gave Doc the opportunity to pull one of the most brazen and successful defensive bluffs I can recall.

As I stood behind him, I wondered what he would lead to the second trick. What would I lead? What would you lead? Surely there was no hope of beating 4 Spades?

It was inconceivable that a trump lead could do any good, even though in theory it would cut down dummy's ruffing power. But South wouldn't need any ruffing power, not with all those lovely Hearts lined up for the taking. If a trump were returned at trick 2, South would win with the Ace, overtake the Queen with his King, draw the last trump with the Jack, and play the Hearts for 2 overtricks.

Another Diamond, then, with the idea of forcing the dummy? Same thing, I thought. Ruff with the Ace, cash the Queen, get back to hand with the Ace of Hearts, draw the rest of the trumps, then enjoy the Hearts as before.

And there seemed little or no point in playing a Heart or Club because . . . my reverie was interrupted at that point by South, who at last played dummy's Diamond. Doc put up the Ace, then with scarcely a pause, led back the 3 of Hearts!

I caught sight of South's expression, full of anxiety and suspicion. He looked intently at that innocent little trey, and tried to figure out what sinister implications lay behind it. Here was an apparent gift which would solve any riddles about the distribution of the adverse Hearts. But what if West had the Jack and refused to cover South's 9? The suit would be blocked. At last, South came back to the decision he had first made: Doc had a singleton Heart, and was hoping to find West with the Ace and get in a Heart ruff before trumps were drawn.

So poor South refused the Greek gift of the free finesse, un-blocked by playing his Ace, crossed to dummy's Ace of trumps and followed with the Queen. He overtook this with his King, smiling smugly now as both East and West followed with a second trump. Then the Jack of trumps drew West's last trump, and the stage was set for the master-stroke.

Doc had apparently lost interest now. He had slumped back in his chair, and was glancing morosely at the other tables. South played the 9 of Hearts, and called for dummy's 10. Apathetically, Doc withdrew a card, and as South stretched out a hand to grab for the trick, Doc suddenly sprang alive. With a whirling movement of his arm, he slapped the Jack of Hearts hard against his own forehead, where it stuck like a bright medallion, the brilliant red of the card's pattern lighting up the weathered old forehead.

Then he gently detached the card, placed it over the 10, gathered up the trick, and in quick succession played the King of Diamonds and the Ace of Clubs.

"One down," he said crisply.

"Hard luck, partner," said North tartly.

"Brilliant," said West gleefully.

South, whose circulation was only just beginning to start up again, said nothing for a long moment. Then, putting on a brave smile, he found his voice.

"Maybe I should take up minin'," he said.

Born Lucky

It is better to be born lucky than rich, runs the old saying. Not many bridge players will dispute this, because there's no point in being born rich if a lifetime's succession of bad hands and idiotic partners is going to reduce you to poverty. What's more, there's something vaguely disreputable about being a known poor cardholder, while if you're known to be lucky in that respect, not only does your popularity rise out of all proportion, but you get to play more hands.

The luckiest player I ever knew was called Morry. Maybe he had another name, like Maurice or Morris; maybe Morry is an old Hebrew word meaning "he who can do no wrong with the cards." But I never heard him called anything but Morry, and he was fantastically lucky. It was a common sight in the club to which we both belonged to see a member enter the card room, catch sight of Morry, then hurry over to rub his coat, a superstition considered to have the power to transfer some of the famous luck to the person making contact. There was no scientific basis to this little piece of mythology, but it sure made you feel a whole lot better.

In addition to his legendary luck, Morry was also no mean manipulator of the cards, so he was everybody's favorite partner. I frequently played opposite him, and found him very easy to get along with, despite his habit of riding his luck to the full. His bidding was usually on the forward side, to say the least, and although he occasionally got himself into some atrocious

145

contracts, his opponents never seemed to learn the folly of doubling him. Maybe he had a deep instinctive judgment for such situations, or maybe it was just that he liked to stick out his neck only to see someone throw a gold chain around it instead of a noose.

One such instance took place at the club on New Year's Eve. There was a little tradition at the club which had been going on for years and which was very popular. A small sum was added to the card fees every session, and this went into the Grand Slam kitty. Whenever a pair bid and made a grand slam, they shared the proceeds. If the end of the year came along and the kitty had not been won, the proceeds went to charity, and the kitty started again in the New Year.

On this occasion the kitty was very sizeable—well over the equivalent of a month's wages. Many pairs had bid 6 and made 7, and several had bid 7, only to make 6, but for a long time the kitty had burgeoned undisturbed. Now that New Year's Eve had arrived, this was the last chance. All the members at the club that night were keenly aware of this, and any pair whose combined holding justified bidding 6 were apt to take a glance at the large plastic box full of notes and coins, take a deep breath, and bid one more just in case.

It got to about 11:50, and the club secretary had just called "Last hand, ladies and gentlemen, please." I had just finished a rubber, so I strolled round the room watching the play. Then I became aware of a noticeable air of tension over at Morry's table, and the number of kibitzers grew even as I watched. I went over to join them. Morry sat in the South seat on this deal, which West had just dealt at game-all.

```
            ♠ 7 6
            ♡ A Q 7 4
            ◇ A K Q 2
            ♣ 6 5 3

♠ K Q J 10 9 8 2    ┌─────────┐    ♠ none
♡ 10 8 6            │    N    │    ♡ J 9 3 2
◇ 10 9 3           W│       │E   ◇ J 8 7 5
♣ none              │    S    │    ♣ 10 9 8 7 4
                    └─────────┘
            ♠ A 5 4 3
            ♡ K 5
            ◇ 6 4
            ♣ A K Q J 2
```

The bidding surged along on a tide of breathless optimism:

W	N	E	S
3♠	dble	pass	4♠
pass	5◇	pass	5♠
pass	6♡	pass	7♣
pass	pass	dble	7 NT
pass	pass	dble	all pass

West thought for no more than 2 seconds before leading the King of Spades, but when dummy went down, and Morry called for a small Spade, it took East much longer than 2 minutes to extract a card from his hand. In fact, he was already squeezed, half-way through Trick 1!

Eventually, his brow furrowed with anxiety, East threw a Heart. Morry won the trick, played the King of Hearts, then the Ace and Queen, whereupon he found that dummy had the 13th Heart. So he played that too.

Again East was squeezed. This time a Club went. So Morry, who could count, was able to put down his cards and claim. He then drew from his pocket a large and expensive cigar, which he ceremoniously lit, taking his time, while East lambasted West and the club secretary staggered over to the table with the enormous kitty.

"What happens if I lead a Heart or Diamond?" asked West, who was aware of the damage his Spade lead had caused, and was anxious to rehabilitate himself in front of the kibitzers.

"Good question," said Morry equably. "Let's see, shall we?"

He had started to count his huge pile of winnings, but he pushed his loot aside to make room for the cards.

"Heart or Diamond lead. Makes no difference which, as far as I can tell. Let's say a Heart. My King wins, and I play a Club and West shows out. What do I do next? Play some Clubs, I suppose. What are we down to after the Heart lead, four rounds of Clubs and three Diamonds?"

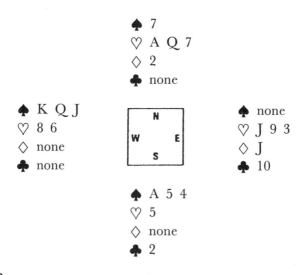

```
                    ♠ 7
                    ♡ A Q 7
                    ◇ 2
                    ♣ none

   ♠ K Q J        ┌──────────┐       ♠ none
   ♡ 8 6          │    N     │       ♡ J 9 3
   ◇ none         │ W      E │       ◇ J
   ♣ none         │    S     │       ♣ 10
                  └──────────┘
                    ♠ A 5 4
                    ♡ 5
                    ◇ none
                    ♣ 2
```

"So now I play a Spade. East throws his Club, so I get an extra Club trick, but it doesn't do me much good, because when I play my deuce of Clubs, dummy has to discard before East, who will simply throw whatever suit dummy throws, and there's no more squeezing, except that your old Uncle Morry here is squeezed out of this handsome pile of lucre."

He glanced at his watch before resuming counting. "Past midnight," he announced. Then, turning to the gallery of members who had been watching with a mixture of envy and incredulity, he said cheerfully, "Happy New Year, fellers, and keep right on doubling."

The Little Old Ladies Strike Again

The Blue Valley Bridge Club had earned itself a reputation for good quality bridge, efficiently organized competitions, and a high standard of decorum. If you asked any Blue Valley member how this had been achieved, he would tell you, "Ralph Carver." The Club's committee had appointed Carver a few years previously as full-time secretary and tournament director. It was a resoundingly successful appointment.

Ralph Carver liked to keep his members happy, but he also aimed to keep their bridge horizons continually expanding. He was known as an innovator, and his latest addition to the range of tournaments, which had been instituted two years ago, was extremely popular already. Known as the Special Hands event, it was run like an ordinary duplicate pairs, except that the hands were pre-set. Some of them were drawn from Carver's own voluminous files, and some of them had been constructed by him with the event in mind. Each player was presented with a booklet at the conclusion of the event, and the foreword contained this remark: "Each hand has been selected on the basis that it gives equal scope to both pairs for a good result."

He might have added that another good result was an evening crammed with sparkling and scintillating bridge, and an enthusiastic capacity attendance. Here is a typical Carver deal:

East-West: Vulnerable
Dealer: North

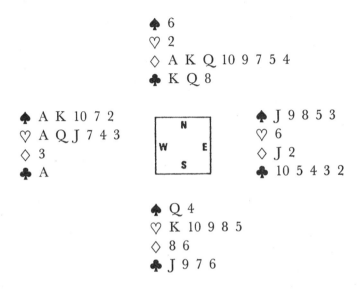

♠ 6
♡ 2
♢ A K Q 10 9 7 5 4
♣ K Q 8

♠ A K 10 7 2
♡ A Q J 7 4 3
♢ 3
♣ A

♠ J 9 8 5 3
♡ 6
♢ J 2
♣ 10 5 4 3 2

♠ Q 4
♡ K 10 9 8 5
♢ 8 6
♣ J 9 7 6

If North opened a tame 1 Diamond, East-West would have no difficulty in reaching 4 Spades, and might even get to the slam. But where North took the bull by the horns and leapt to 4 or even 5 Diamonds at his first bid, West had a finely balanced decision to make.

It was this carefully calculated balance of the opposing forces which made the event so popular, and which made winning it such an enviable triumph for the successful pair. Most of the travelling scoresheets showed a cluster of scores around the average, with only rarely a clear top. One of these exceptions caused much controversy, and gave Carver quite a headache.

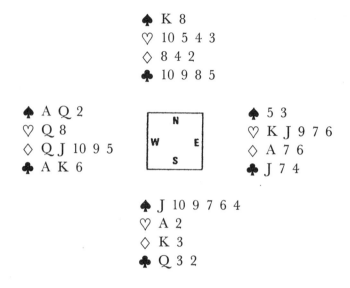

```
                ♠ K 8
                ♡ 10 5 4 3
                ◇ 8 4 2
                ♣ 10 9 8 5

♠ A Q 2                           ♠ 5 3
♡ Q 8            ┌─────────┐      ♡ K J 9 7 6
◇ Q J 10 9 5     │    N    │      ◇ A 7 6
♣ A K 6          │ W     E │      ♣ J 7 4
                 │    S    │
                 └─────────┘
                ♠ J 10 9 7 6 4
                ♡ A 2
                ◇ K 3
                ♣ Q 3 2
```

West dealt at love-all, and a predictable sequence was:

W	N	E	S
1 ◇	pass	1 ♡	1 ♠
2 NT	pass	3 NT	all pass

North led the King of Spades, and whether or not West ducked the first lead, he soon found himself on lead after having won a Spade trick. A quick count showed 9 tricks: 2 Spades, at least one Heart, 4 Diamonds and 2 Clubs. A more sober review revealed that in the process, South would get the lead twice, with the Ace of Hearts and the King of Diamonds. On the first occasion he would be able to set up his suit, and when he was in the second time, he would run it; the 9 tricks would never materialize.

So various Wests found various ways to circumvent disaster. One line of attack which yielded fruit was this: go to dummy's

Ace of Diamonds and lead a small Heart. If South played the deuce, the Heart trick was in the bag, and West could then start on the Diamonds—Queen first—with every confidence of making 9 tricks.

If South jumped straight in with the Ace of Hearts when a small Heart was led from dummy, a wily West would drop the Queen. After winning the Spade return, West would play his 8 of Hearts to dummy's 9. When that held, he would resume breathing, then run the Hearts. Depending on South's discards, West would make either 9 or 10 tricks.

When the travelling scoresheet had completed its rounds, that in fact was the picture it showed: 3 NT by West, either just made or made with one overtrick. There was just one exception.

"Hallo!" exclaimed Carver as he scanned the scoresheet. "What caused that?"

He was looking at an entry which showed that 3 NT by West had gone 3 down.

"Who's Pair 12 North-South?" he asked his assistant.

It turned out that North-South consisted of two little old ladies.

"I might have known it," sighed Carver. "What did they get up to this time?"

The assistant went in search of them, but apparently they had gone home immediately after the 'last hand had been played. Carver sought out their East-West opponents who had contributed to that mystifying result, and asked them what had happened to upset 3 NT so catastrophically.

"It can't be made," said West.

"Can't be made! Everybody else made it; half of them with an overtrick."

"I find that difficult to believe," said West.

"What was the bidding?" asked Carver.

"Let me see the hands again and I'll tell you. Ah, yes. 1 Diamond from me, 1 Heart by East, 2 NT from me, 3 NT by East."

"Wait a minute. Are you telling me South didn't come in with a Spade bid?"

"That's right. No intervening bid at all."

"So the opening lead . . .?"

"Was the 10 of Clubs."

They looked at the hands again, trying to apply a fresh perspective. There was a huge difference. With no special threat to the hand, West put in dummy's Jack of Clubs; it was covered by South's Queen and taken by West's King. Now West led the Queen of Hearts, losing to South's Ace. Then—West remembered this vividly—South had led not the Jack of Spades, but the 7. Such an innocent card.

West tried the Queen and lost to North's King. The 8 of Spades had come back, South put in the Jack, and West— with nothing about the play of the suit to suggest a 6–2 distribution—had taken the Ace.

At that stage, West had decided to take the Diamond finesse; he remembered that he had no special qualms about it. He ran the Queen, losing to South's King, and got a horrible shock when North discarded on the Spade return. Altogether, the defence took 5 Spade tricks, the Ace of Hearts and the King of Diamonds.

Ralph Carver felt suddenly sorry for West.

"Of course, you realize this isn't a par contest," he said. "If it were, I should oblige South to bid 1 Spade, then you'd be warned. I wonder why she didn't bid a Spade, anyway."

He made a point of cornering the little old ladies when they arrived for the next weekly duplicate.

"Good evening, Mrs. Wintringham; nice to see you, Mrs. Hamilton."

The ladies beamed.

"Tell me," went on Carver, "I don't suppose you happen to remember which of you was North and which was South last week in the Special Hands event?"

"Why, I was South," said Mrs. Hamilton. "I remember quite clearly, because Nora there had to write down the scores. I hope nothing's wrong?"

"Not exactly. But I'd be glad if you'd clear up something for me. It's been bothering me all week."

He held 13 cards in his hand, and now he spread them face upwards on a table.

"This is a hand from last week," he said. "It's one of the hands you held. You're South. West deals and bids 1 Diamond. North passes, and East says 1 Heart. What do you bid?"

"Why, 1 Spade, of course!" sang out both ladies in unison.

"I give up," said Carver, and went away, clutching his head.

"What do you think can be troubling poor Mr. Carver?" said Mrs. Wintringham.

"He's probably been working too hard," said Mrs. Hamilton. "And don't forget, he has some very peculiar people to put up with."

A Bitter Goulash

When the cards are dealt in bunches instead of one at a time, the deal is called a goulash. This form of dealing is forbidden by the Laws of Contract Bridge, but from time to time a light-hearted rubber bridge session has been known to see the practice indulged in, usually to get a little more pep out of the cards.

The predictable effect of a goulash is, of course, that of freakish distribution, especially when the deal is preceded by only a cursory shuffle, or no shuffle at all. Very long suits and voids are no longer the exceptions: they become normal.

Some years ago a young man, who had better remain name-less, was in the habit of complaining frequently about the dull and drab hands which seemed to predominate in the weekly duplicate tournaments held at his club. It seemed to him that he took part in an unending succession of uninspiring part-scores, cold game contracts where there was no scope for either the declarer or the defence to do anything interesting, and even a proportion of throw-ins. Youth being what it is, the young man yearned for action, and to him action meant the excitement of long suits, competitive auctions, slams, pre-empts and dramatic overcalls.

One evening he arrived at his club earlier than usual, and found himself the only member there. The duplicate boards were spread around the tables with last week's cards still in them, awaiting re-dealing for the evening's play. A custom common to many small clubs was practiced at this one: the early arrivals would re-deal the boards, saving time later on. So the young man seated himself at the nearest table and started taking out the cards, shuffling them and dealing them before stowing them away again in their slots in the boards.

As he finished one deal, he contemplated the backs of the cards moodily. "Another throw-in right there," he thought. "Or 1 Diamond bid and made. Big deal." What wouldn't he give for a genuine big deal. Suddenly he brightened as a new thought hit him. Why shouldn't he engineer a big deal himself? He was still alone. Swiftly he stripped the next board of its cards, and immediately dealt them in two lots of six and a one. Then stacking the four sets of cards in neat piles, he pushed them into their slots face downward, because although he had a wayward streak, he was no cheat. But he couldn't help but notice that it was Board 21 that now held the goulash.

Shortly after that, some members strolled in; before very long, the tournament started. For once, the young man and his slightly older partner were having a good session; they were playing steady bridge and getting regularly good results. By the time the move was called for the last round, they reckoned that, provided they could avoid outright disaster, they would be in line for one of the top awards.

As they settled themselves in the North-South seats for the final round, the young man's pulse quickened as he saw they were going to play boards 19–21. But Board 19 was thrown in, to their disgust, and to their greater disgust they saw on examining the travelling scoresheet that most East-West pairs had ventured a bid, got too high, gone down a trick or two, and had donated their North-South opponents a long list of 50's and 100's. They sadly entered their lowly score on their own card.

Board 20 turned out to be an easy game. North opened 1 NT and the young man responded 3 NT. North made his contract with an overtrick, then eagerly snatching the score-sheet out of the board, he found that every single North had scored exactly the same number of tricks in the same contract. Dead flat board.

Then came Board 21. Although the young man could only see the South cards, the full deal was:

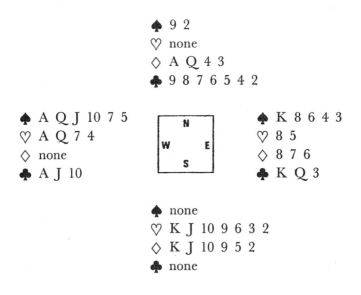

```
                    ♠ 9 2
                    ♡ none
                    ◇ A Q 4 3
                    ♣ 9 8 7 6 5 4 2

♠ A Q J 10 7 5                          ♠ K 8 6 4 3
♡ A Q 7 4                               ♡ 8 5
◇ none              W        E          ◇ 8 7 6
♣ A J 10                                ♣ K Q 3

                    ♠ none
                    ♡ K J 10 9 6 3 2
                    ◇ K J 10 9 5 2
                    ♣ none
```

At game-all, with West the dealer, the bidding began:

W	N	E	S
2 ♠	pass	4 ♠	?

The young man stirred uneasily in his seat. He had wanted action, and here it was. But what kind of action was going to get the best result here? Was North sitting over there with a

Spade trick and an outside Ace, ready to crack a 6 Spade contract? Did his partner have a worthless hand in defence, but a useful red card or two? Pure guesswork. One thing he was sure of: East and West were on their way to a Spade slam, and somehow he had to deflect them. There seemed no point in pussyfooting around at the 4-level. He decided to crash incontinently into the 6-level himself. He looked at his array of Hearts and Diamonds and thought ruefully, "Caught red-handed."

Well, Hearts were not only the higher suit but also the longer suit. Hardly a matter for choice. "Six Hearts," he said.

West gave this some consideration, and finally doubled. There was no further bidding. The Ace of Spades was led, and when the young man saw his dummy, his heart plummeted into his belly. What an idiotic idea it had been to fool around with the cards. There was no way to avoid two trump losers. One down, doubled.

The players spread their cards out on the table, and as he examined them, his spirits rose again. "Partner, they can make 6 Spades!" he exclaimed. "No—seven! They had a Grand Slam. This is a good one for us." And he grabbed the travelling scoresheet.

Every South player had sacrificed in 7 Diamonds over 6 Spades, and every West had decided to double rather than embark on a grand slam which seemed at best speculative. Worse—far worse—every South player had made his doubled contract for a huge score. The young man, morose and contrite now, watched as his partner entered the details on the sheet. He apologized once more for his wild jump into 6 Hearts. His partner looked up from the scoresheet, smiling his forgiveness.

"Forget it," he said. "These things happen. It was just one of those hands where the devil got into the cards."

Kibitzer, Kibitzer, Where Have You Been?

Seven men were in the room. Four of them sat at the brightly lit card table, while the other three roamed around moodily, emerging from the shadows to watch one of the players in action, then congregating in a corner to complain bitterly to one another. It had been a very long rubber: well over an hour, in fact, and as this was before the introduction of the "Chicago" method of playing rubber bridge, none of them knew whether a further hour of delay and frustration lay in wait.

"George is never going to make 4 Hearts," said one of the kibitzers, a man called Bert, in soft but scornful tones. "He can look at his cards all night, but he's got four losers, and that's that."

Bert was right. George went on playing out all his trumps, clinging obstinately to his King of Clubs, just in case a squeeze or even a pseudo-squeeze developed. But the man with the Ace of Clubs was not under the remotest pressure, and as he took the setting trick he said: "I kept it specially for you, George; don't look so disappointed."

The players laughed good-naturedly, but no laughter came from the three men standing round the table.

"Come on, you guys," said Bert irritably, "get the next hand dealt. Let's see if you can bid what you can make, then make what you've bid, just for a change."

"OK," said George, who occupied the South seat. "C'mon,

fellers, the gallery's getting critical. Next thing, they'll be asking for their money back."

It had been game-all for some time, and after West had dealt, George picked up his cards and gazed at this dismal collection:

♠ 9 8 7 6
♡ 9
♢ 6 5 4 3 2
♣ 5 4 2

Now they won't have long to wait, he thought. Must be at least a game in this for East and West. Maybe even a slam. Trying to keep the pessimism out of his face, he waited for West to bid.

West opened the bidding with 1 Heart. North doubled. East redoubled, which didn't surprise George. In the circumstances, he felt he couldn't contribute anything to the auction; let partner rescue himself.

West also passed, and North now bid 1 NT, which was again doubled by East.

"Now I must bid," thought George, and he decided that it would be marginally less dangerous to bid 2 Diamonds than 2 Spades. If they doubled 2 Diamonds, and partner himself retreated to Spades, he could scarcely hope for any strength, but four trumps and a singleton would be something of a life-saver.

Over George's 2 Diamonds, however, West came back with 2 Hearts. North, glaring defiance at the sullen kibitzers, bid 3 Diamonds, which was promptly doubled by East, and there were then three passes.

"My lead?" asked West. He gave the matter prolonged

thought, while the trio of kibitzers made a rapid circuit of the table. This is what they saw:

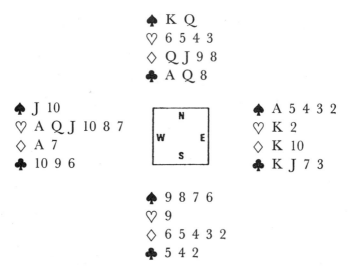

```
                    ♠ K Q
                    ♡ 6 5 4 3
                    ◇ Q J 9 8
                    ♣ A Q 8
  ♠ J 10                              ♠ A 5 4 3 2
  ♡ A Q J 10 8 7      N               ♡ K 2
  ◇ A 7           W       E           ◇ K 10
  ♣ 10 9 6           S                ♣ K J 7 3
                    ♠ 9 8 7 6
                    ♡ 9
                    ◇ 6 5 4 3 2
                    ♣ 5 4 2
```

Bert paused behind George's chair, and his brow furrowed at the sight of that barren vista. "For heaven's sake!" he exploded, "Down again. Somebody round here's got the idea that a rubber's supposed to last all night. I'm going into the next room to fix myself a real strong drink. Sorry, George," he added, "but he's killed you again on this one." And he stumped out of the room.

Meanwhile, West had made up his mind, and he led the Ace of Diamonds. George surveyed the dummy without enthusiasm. He could see that East-West had 26 points between them, but, he reminded himself, this isn't duplicate, it's just another of North's notorious sacrifices.

West continued with another trump, won by East's king. East pushed back the King of Hearts, and West overtook with the Ace, continuing with the Queen, which George ruffed.

Now a Spade was led to dummy's King and East's Ace; East, who could scarcely do otherwise, returned a Spade. But as the trick was collected, George noted with incredulity that all the five Spade honors had fallen in the space of two tricks. That's different, he thought.

He ruffed himself back to his hand with another Heart, then led the 9 and 8 of Spades, throwing the 8 then the Queen of Clubs from dummy. The Ace of Clubs was followed by dummy's last Heart, ruffed by George's last trump, and dummy's only remaining cards were the Queen and Jack of trumps. Victory!

Both East and West started mumbling, then changed to a sharper squawking as it was pointed out that 4 Hearts was makeable for them, but the hand had had the effect of subduing them, and their voices trailed away. Silence fell over the table, and into the silence strode Bert, glass in hand. He had been wondering how many tricks George had gone down. "Two or three?" he asked brusquely.

George, who had been working out the score, thought he was being asked whether the contract was 2 or 3 Diamonds doubled.

"Three," he answered, and went on with his arithmetic.

"Sheer, reckless irresponsibility," said Bert sternly to North. "Why condemn the man to play at the 3-level when the bidding tells you he can't have more than a Queen at the most, and when you're certain to get doubled? Why not just let them make their 4 Hearts? That wouldn't cost you much more than you just gave away, plus it would get the rubber over. It's rough, y'know, hanging around all night while you—"

He broke off. The other two kibitzers, grinning at him, were taking their seats at the table, while some of the original occupants were rising and stretching themselves. George went over to Bert, and put an arm gently round his shoulder.

"We've just devised a new rule," he said. "We're going to put it up to the Portland Club and the ACBL and ask them to adopt it officially. Let me tell you about it. It applies only to holders of Yarboroughs who get doubled in 3 Diamonds and then make their contract. The rule states that any kibitzer who openly doubts the ability of the declarer to make his contract shall be required to sit out the next three rubbers as a penalty. Moreover—"

"You putting me on? You ain't telling me you actually made 3 Diamonds just now? With that rubbish?"

"Rubbish?" said George. "You didn't notice my two master Spades? Meanwhile, you're holding up the game. You know how strongly some people feel about that. I think I'll just fix myself a strong drink. Something tells me I need it more than you do."

Some People Never Learn

The two of them entered the card room together, a large and voluble man with a commanding air talking earnestly to his companion, a pale, thin, worried-looking young man. The large man steered the other over to a corner table, and with the air of a conspirator, said:

"Now remember, open 5-card majors, don't overcall without a good strong suit, keep out of no trumps with a singleton, lead Ace from Ace-King, we play optional doubles over pre-empts, lead a high card if you just want to get off lead and a low one if you want the suit returned, you need a stopper in every suit for an opening 1 NT, remember Stayman is non-forcing with us, all twos are strong, Blackwood, and bid to the score when we have a partial. Got all that?"

"Er—."

"Come on," snapped the large man impatiently, "they're waiting for us at that table over there."

Two ladies of indeterminate age bestowed glacial smiles as the men approached. Perfunctory greetings and introductions were exchanged, then the cut was made, the young man sitting North and starting to deal the cards slowly and carefully, as if this was a feat of some complexity. When he had dealt the last card, the other three at the table swept their cards briskly into their hands, and had them sorted in five seconds flat.

"Your call, young man," said one of the ladies imperiously, noting with contempt that the young man was still jabbing cards in and out from one place to another and back again. This was the deal:

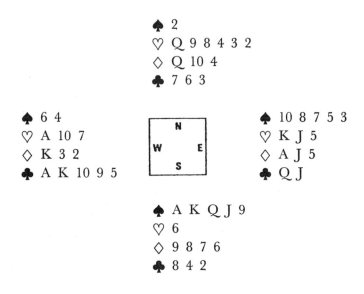

♠ 2
♡ Q 9 8 4 3 2
◇ Q 10 4
♣ 7 6 3

♠ 6 4
♡ A 10 7
◇ K 3 2
♣ A K 10 9 5

♠ 10 8 7 5 3
♡ K J 5
◇ A J 5
♣ Q J

♠ A K Q J 9
♡ 6
◇ 9 8 7 6
♣ 8 4 2

With the ladies sitting East and West, the bidding was:

N	E	S	W
pass	1 ♠	pass	3 NT
pass	pass	dble	all pass

The young man with the North cards was a little surprised to hear his partner double, but South was such a good player that it could be presumed that he knew what he was doing. North had been tutored to lead the fourth highest of his longest, so out came the 4 of Hearts. After having inspected dummy, North looked casually across the table at his partner, and was shocked to see the murderous expression that met him. Bewildered and chastened, he put his eyes down amongst his cards, and prepared to defend with all his accumulated six months of experience.

But the play was a formality. West lost no time in making 3 Hearts, 5 Clubs and 2 Diamonds for a doubled overtrick.

"Partner," said South in injured tones, "don't you know what that double means?"

"It means you expect to beat their contract," said North.

"It means that you are required to lead the suit first bid by dummy," said South severely. "If you had led your Spade, we make the first 5 tricks."

"Sorry partner," said North. "I'll try to remember."

The very next hand came out like this:

```
                    ♠ 8 6 5 4
                    ♡ A J 10 9 3
                    ◇ 6
                    ♣ 8 6 3


♠ A Q 10 2          ┌──────────┐         ♠ 7
♡ 8 5 4             │    N     │         ♡ 7 2
◇ A 2               │ W     E  │         ◇ Q J 10 9 7 5 4 3
♣ K J 10 7          │    S     │         ♣ A 2
                    └──────────┘

                    ♠ K J 9 3
                    ♡ K Q 6
                    ◇ K 8
                    ♣ Q 9 5 4
```

With East the dealer, the bidding went like this:

E	S	W	N
3 ◇	pass	3 NT	pass
pass	dble		all pass

So young North found himself on lead against the same contract, doubled by the same irascible partner, but this time he knew what to do. Singleton or not, he was not going to make the same mistake twice. Proudly he flipped his 6 of Diamonds on to the table, down went dummy, and up went South's temperature. Beads of perspiration formed on his brow; soundless words twisted his mouth out of shape.

Meanwhile, West pursed her lips into the nearest she could get to a smile, and thanked her partner. Then she played dummy's Queen of Diamonds. South played low, hoping against hope that North held a doubleton, but West produced the deuce. West then cashed her Ace of Diamonds, bringing down South's King, crossed to dummy's Ace of Clubs, and ran the Diamonds. South couldn't cope with the long discarding process, and West eventually made all 13 tricks.

"Table!" called East loudly, and two other ladies made their way towards them. North and South paid up, North looking pained, South grunting and snorting. The four ladies spread the deck for the cut, and made polite noises to each other. Then one of them said: "Those last opponents of yours didn't stay long."

They all looked towards the door. The large man was wagging an earnest finger at the younger man, and talking in his court-martial voice. Before the door closed behind them, three words could be discerned: ". . . you must remember . . ."

Some people never learn, and it's often because some people never teach them properly.

A Gentle Dip in Shark-Infested Waters

PA-LOO'-KA (n): a bridge novice; one who is allowed to play only on sufferance, and who is expected to lose consistently, in accordance with his lowly status.

SHARK (n): a money-bridge player, noted for ruthlessness and cunning; one who lurks near the high-stake table; one who feeds on a diet of palookas.

Some years ago, at a fashionable London bridge club, a pair of sharks in search of prey found a couple of young men sitting respectfully apart from the players. The sharks began an ingratiating conversation. It appeared that the young men were palookas, and had really only been allowed to join the club because they were well connected. The sharks exchanged hungry glances; their teeth glinted savagely for a moment, and their eyes narrowed purposefully. Then, assuming their masks of benevolence again, they suggested a friendly rubber or two. The young men, flattered and excited, agreed readily, and agreed also to the unusually high stakes suggested by one of the sharks. With the palookas in the North-South seats, the rubber began.

Now, you will agree that it is one thing to lam the living daylights out of a pair of palookas, but it is quite another thing altogether to browbeat a deck of cards into giving you the necessary goodies to do it with. On the first two hands, the palookas blundered their way into makeable game contracts, then failed to do anything drastically wrong in the play, so

169

that they were adding up the points for rubber before the sharks had drawn breath.

Mastering their resentment, the sharks suggested a second rubber, and the palookas agreed. It seemed only fair. There were four deals in the second rubber: twice the young men settled for undoubled penalties for defeating atrocious overcalls, and twice they held the cards for a cold slam without having the faintest notion of how to bid it. They stayed meekly in game both times. Just over half an hour had gone by since they sat down to play, and they were 2,500 points ahead.

The sharks did not appear to share their happiness. This was not the kind of treatment they were accustomed to. In fact, their faces took on such fierce and vengeful expressions that a small gallery of onlookers drifted towards the table to watch the third rubber.

On the very first hand, the palookas held a combined 29-count, and ignoring a barrage of interference bids throughout the auction, got to 5 Clubs and made it. On the next hand, a shark, desperation distorting his judgment, stuck his neck out much too far, and one of the palookas, apologetic and deferential, went so far as to double him in 4 Diamonds. That netted a further 500.

The partner of the doubled shark, seeking some way to redress this insult, tried a psychic opening bid second in hand. This was innocently doubled for a take-out, but was never taken out. The gallery grinned. The palookas raked in 300 more. The sharks gritted their teeth in a frenzy of frustration, and glared around them malevolently.

At last their turn came. With a change of luck they bid and made game easily. So it was now game-all. But a disaster lay in wait. They reached 4 Spades on the very next hand, but an opening lead from a palooka, which was so ignorant as to be almost uncouth, proved to be the only way to set the contract. The gallery broke out in unconcealed applause. The sharks, looking gaunt and dishevelled, licked dry lips, and below the table their fists were tightly clenched. And then . . .

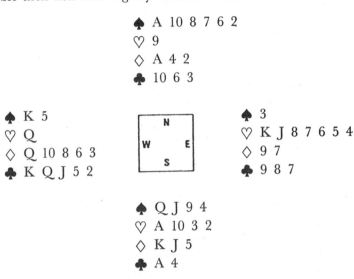

♠ A 10 8 7 6 2
♡ 9
◇ A 4 2
♣ 10 6 3

♠ K 5
♡ Q
◇ Q 10 8 6 3
♣ K Q J 5 2

♠ 3
♡ K J 8 7 6 5 4
◇ 9 7
♣ 9 8 7

♠ Q J 9 4
♡ A 10 3 2
◇ K J 5
♣ A 4

The palooka in the South seat had just acquired the notion of what was known in those days as the "short Club"; his partner had never heard of it. The bidding staggered along like this:

S	W	N	E
1 ♣(1)	1 ◇(2)	1 ♠	2 ♡
2 NT	pass(3)	3 ♣(4)	3 ♡
3 NT(5)	pass	4 ♣(6)	4 ♡
4 NT(7)	pass	5 ♡(8)	dble
5 NT(9)	dble(10)	all pass	

At intervals denoted by the numbers against some of the bids, the unspoken thoughts of the players concerned were:

(1) Here's a chance to use that short-Club gadget.

(2) These kids are psyche-resistant; let's play natural.

(3) Let's hope they stay there.

(4) We can't stay there; with a singleton, and three of my partner's suit, I'll have to heave him out of NT.

(5) Why doesn't he leave me in NT?

(6) He doesn't seem to understand; he can't support my suit, so I've got to support his.

(7) Why doesn't he leave me in NT?

(8) This is the Blackwood caper. Two Aces, partner.

(9) Why doesn't he leave me in NT?

(10) Gotcha!

The Western shark led the Queen of Hearts; East played low, and South, playing almost purely by instinct, did likewise. Next came the King of Clubs, and again South ducked, but he had to take the next trick with his Ace of Clubs.

Now South produced the Queen of Spades, and West, with an expression of utter indifference, donated the 5. The declarer's hand hovered up and down over the strung-out Spade suit in dummy, going from the 2 to the Ace and back again, while the gallery held its collective breath. Eventually, annoyed at his own indecision, declarer reached right across and tapped the top of the table just above the Ace of Spades. Like an automatic reflex, East's 3 of Spades shot out of his hand before he knew what he was doing. Thoughtfully, declarer played low from dummy, while strange choking sounds came from West.

All the Spades were played off, leaving:

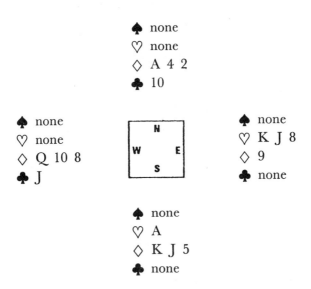

♠ none
♡ none
◇ A 4 2
♣ 10

♠ none
♡ none
◇ Q 10 8
♣ J

N
W   E
S

♠ none
♡ K J 8
◇ 9
♣ none

♠ none
♡ A
◇ K J 5
♣ none

A small Diamond was played to the King, then the Ace of Hearts was cashed, the gallery nodding approvingly, like tulips in a breeze.

The Western shark, boiling with fury, let go his 10 of Diamonds, and the Ace and Jack took the last two tricks. The gallery broke out into loud congratulations, the sharks slumped back in their seats, utterly demoralized, while the two palookas busily occupied themselves by adding up the score for game and rubber. North looked up from his arithmetic for a moment and said:

"If he doesn't double your 5 No Trump bid, I'm all set to bid 6 Clubs."

The sharks, pale and crumpled, got slowly to their feet, threw some money onto the table, and walked unsteadily from the room.

Whence All But He Had Fled

The folk tales of every country contain examples of courage bordering on reckless folly. But not only the folk tales. Any bridge player who's been around for long enough will have an impressive anthology of bravery and bravado, heroism and hysteria. And the striking thing is that while the folk tales will have been so encrusted with legend as to be unrecognizable to the original participants, the bridge stories will be true. The exploits of such as Davy Crockett, Robin Hood and Casey Jones have been suitably embroidered over the years, but the bridge player knows there's no need to embellish a plain tale.

Finding myself at a hotel in strange territory one night, I was relieved to discover that a game of bridge was going on. When I took my place at the table, I cut as my partner a beardless boy, a fresh-faced stripling scarcely out of school. The rubber was an unusually long one, and by the time we got to the hand I am about to describe, I should not have been at all surprised to find that my partner was in direct line of · descent from the boy who stood on the burning deck. The only difference was that this one had a little more luck. He needed it.

With game to our side, he sat South; our opponents were competent performers, though slightly on the forward side with their bidding. I dealt, and as the auction proceeded, it was accompanied by a series of unspoken *obbligatos*, which I reproduce here.

First, the hand:

174

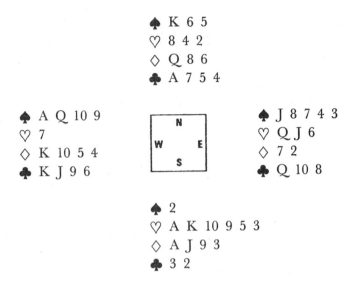

♠ K 6 5
♡ 8 4 2
◇ Q 8 6
♣ A 7 5 4

♠ A Q 10 9
♡ 7
◇ K 10 5 4
♣ K J 9 6

♠ J 8 7 4 3
♡ Q J 6
◇ 7 2
♣ Q 10 8

♠ 2
♡ A K 10 9 5 3
◇ A J 9 3
♣ 3 2

NORTH: The way things are going, he probably won't believe me, but just the same I'm going to PASS.

EAST: I can't do anything with this lot, but maybe partner will turn up with a good hand. I PASS.

SOUTH: I like this hand; just a little in the right place from partner, and we'll be in 4 Hearts. I bid 1 HEART.

WEST: A tiny bit short of points, but distributionally this one's straight out of the textbook. I DOUBLE.

NORTH: I hope partner's got his bid. If so, we've got the balance of the points, plus the box seat. I REDOUBLE.

EAST: I reckon I'm good enough for a free bid here. I say 1 SPADE.

SOUTH: Sorry, partner, but it's gotta be Hearts. I bid 2 HEARTS.

WEST: If he's good enough for a free bid, I'm good enough for a free raise. 2 SPADES.

NORTH: The double doesn't look as appetizing as I thought it might. Partner's got a long Heart suit and not much else. But my few points are all in the right place, and we could well be able to make 9 tricks in NT. I shall bid 2 NT.

EAST: That lets me out. I PASS.

SOUTH: Like I said, it's gotta be Hearts. 3 HEARTS.

WEST: That lets me out. I PASS.

NORTH: Disappointing, but there you are. I shall have to PASS.

EAST: Partner's got some good Spades over there, and probably a singleton Heart. We shouldn't be too badly off in 3 Spades, but the way that kid is bidding, he'll never let us stay there. Let's tempt him. 3 SPADES.

SOUTH: The way that man's bidding, they must have a Spade contract. I bid 4 HEARTS.

WEST: My partner must be unbalanced, either distributionally or mentally. But maybe he's got 6 Spades and a singleton somewhere. Let's see it through. After all, we're not vulnerable. 4 SPADES.

NORTH: No problem. I DOUBLE.

EAST: Oh well. PASS.

SOUTH: Why can't I get my partner to understand? 5 HEARTS.

WEST: Yippee! Now we're out of the fire. DOUBLE.

NORTH: Damn! Now we're back in the fire. I PASS.

EAST: Help yourself to a medal, kid; but this way to the sacrifice first. PASS.

SOUTH: Why is everybody running away? Why all the panic? I PASS.

With the final contract 5 Hearts doubled, West now gave earnest attention to his opening lead. He pulled out the Ace of Spades, then put it back. He fingered a trump, then decided against it. He wondered which of his minor Kings to lead away from. East must have something outside Spades for his free bid. He led the 4 of Diamonds.

I put down my dummy and in icy tones said: "Have fun." Then, unable to restrain my curiosity, I abandoned my rights as dummy and went round behind my partner's chair to see what had been going on, and what was likely to go on now.

What I saw didn't reassure me. A loser in every suit. 2 down doubled, vulnerable, so the bill would be 500. Oh well, he was young, and perhaps he would learn from his mistakes.

But the boy on the burning deck seemed to have little fear of the flames which licked around him. He put in dummy's 8 of Diamonds, and seemed quite prepared to find that it held the trick. He then led dummy's 8 of Hearts, and when East played low, ran it. This, too, he accepted with equanimity. Two tricks with two 8's! I hastily scanned our combined hands to see whether there were any more 8's. No, he would have to make do with old-fashioned Aces and Kings like everybody else.

He then played two more rounds of trumps, East slamming down his Queen and Jack in disgust. Next came the small Spade. West, who was showing signs of nervousness, came straight out with the Ace. He followed this with the Queen of Spades, taken by dummy's King, and the Club loser was discarded.

The flames were now firmly under control. The Diamond King was conceded to the defence and the contract made.

East and West both started snarling at once. It seemed that neither was satisfied with the performance of the other, and it got a bit unpleasant. Looking pained, my partner leaned across the table, and said in the tone of a conspirator, "Seems

177

a shame some people get so worked up about losing a rubber. I mean, when we get the cards, we have to bid them, don't we?"

"WE sure do," I said, letting the emphasis linger on the first word. But I was wasting my time. Armored by optimism and shielded by luck, my young partner had as little time for irony as he had for recriminations. And I liked him for that.

Gathering of the Great

It is difficult for me to be nonchalant about the fact that I took part in the 1972 World Team Olympiad. I looked forward avidly to it for many months, I enjoyed every moment of every match in which I played, and I look back on it with both pride and pleasure. Nonchalance becomes a little easier for me when I contemplate our team's record, but we can't all be winners.

The hands were pre-dealt by computer. In theory there can be no reasonable objection to this practice, but the particular computer used on this occasion seemed to suffer from a lack of seriousness, and instead presented us with a high proportion of quite flippant deals. Never have I seen such a bewildering succession of 8-card suits, 7–6 distributions, voids and power-houses.

When the cards are running wild, it is always a good principle to lean on one's rubber bridge experience. This applies especially to low-level doubles, a much neglected source of profit in the Teams game. An example came up early in our match against the Lebanon team. At love-all, sitting South, I was looking at:

    ♠ 8 7 5
    ♡ Q J 9
    ◇ none
    ♣ A K Q 5 4 3 2

My partner dealt, and opened 1 Diamond. After a pass on

my right, I said 2 Clubs. West bid 2 Spades, and after careful thought, my partner doubled. At first, the decision to pass or to bid on might appear a close one. Two factors came to my aid, one of them a quite old-fashioned rubber bridge principle, the other purely mathematical.

My present partner was also one of my favorite rubber bridge partners, and he and I have for many years regarded the presence of a misfit as the prime reason for resorting to a low-level penalty double. We had the points, of course, but my Diamond void, together with what I could assume was his total lack of interest in Clubs, combined to make the double an attractive proposition.

Secondly, we could hardly go wrong unless there was a slam for our side. Game would net us 400 or so, but even if the double misfired to some extent, we could scarcely get less than 300 from it. But the slam was highly speculative, and in any case, to explore it further would be to give up the certain plus score. I let the double stand, and so did West. The full hand was:

♠ A Q J 9
♡ A 6 4 2
◇ A Q 8 4 2
♣ none

♠ K 10 4 3 2
♡ K 8
◇ K 10 9 7 5
♣ 9

N
W   E
S

♠ 6
♡ 10 7 5 3
◇ J 6 3
♣ J 10 8 7 6

♠ 8 7 5
♡ Q J 9
◇ none
♣ A K Q 5 4 3 2

My partner got off to a fine start with the Ace of Diamonds, and we finished up 900 to the good. The next day I learned that in the Italy vs. U.S.A. match the Americans climbed to 6 Clubs, which of course proved impossible to make, while the Blue Team stayed in 5 Clubs and somehow just made it. But then, they didn't have our West opponent to take the strain off them.

I have two other reminiscences, but they both chiefly concern players, rather than cards. The first exemplifies the impeccable sportsmanship and gentlemanly graciousness of Italy's Blue Team. The other one highlights the buccaneer spirit of one of the game's most colorful personalities.

Among our little squad of happy amateurs there was considerable competition for the privilege of playing in the match against Italy. My delight in learning that I was to be one of the lucky ones was not in the least diluted by the prospect of being taken to the cleaners in the most comprehensive way. David Richardson was my partner. He and I entered the Closed Room to find Belladonna and Avarelli waiting for us, and we were greeted courteously by both of our illustrious opponents. They made an interesting contrast: Belladonna is a swarthy, handsome, mercurial extrovert who combines a boyish sense of humor with the dignity of a statesman; Avarelli, as befits a man who in other circumstances occupies the bench as a high court judge, is taciturn, expressionless, solemn and infallibly polite.

My partner and I had briefly considered making special plans to cope with this formidable pair, but our tactical talk had lasted no more than a minute or two; there didn't seem much point. The Blue Team's record in international matches made a mockery of any such presumptuousness on our part. But I have an obstinate streak which refuses to allow me to acknowledge the cause as lost until it actually is lost. And so it came about that the only time during the whole tournament when I made a psychic bid was against this famous pair.

It happened on one of the very early boards. As the bidding came round to me, it suddenly flashed across my mind that here was a chance not only to snatch a good result on one board, but maybe also to disconcert our opponents sufficiently to restore a little edge to our prospects. I might have saved my time and mental energy, but it was fun while it lasted.

The Italians sat North-South, and with our side vulnerable, East was the dealer. This was the hand:

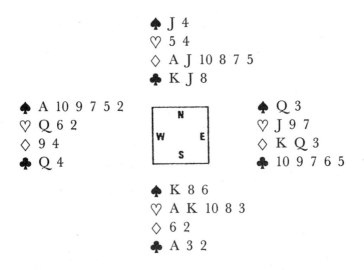

```
                      ♠ J 4
                      ♡ 5 4
                      ◇ A J 10 8 7 5
                      ♣ K J 8
♠ A 10 9 7 5 2                            ♠ Q 3
♡ Q 6 2              ┌──────────┐         ♡ J 9 7
◇ 9 4               │    N     │         ◇ K Q 3
♣ Q 4               │ W      E │         ♣ 10 9 7 6 5
                     │    S     │
                     └──────────┘
                      ♠ K 8 6
                      ♡ A K 10 8 3
                      ◇ 6 2
                      ♣ A 3 2
```

After East's initial pass, Belladonna opened 1 Heart. Sitting West, I thought, "The Blue Team will never credit me with the lèse-majesté to psyche against the Blue Team, especially at unfavorable vulnerability." So I bid 2 Clubs, wondering whether my pounding heart was showing beneath my shirt.

Avarelli bid 2 Diamonds, my trusting partner came in with

3 Clubs and I broke out into a sweat. It may have crossed Belladonna's mind to wonder what had happened to the Spade suit, but he decided to bid 3 NT and leave further action to Avarelli. Avarelli was content to leave things where they stood, though he wasn't anywhere near so content as I was.

My lead of the 10 of Spades was covered by dummy's Jack, East's Queen and South's King. South then took a losing Diamond finesse, and East obediently sent back his other Spade. We made the next 5 tricks with indecent haste, and the contract went 2 down. For a few breathless minutes, we were ahead of Italy!

Belladonna gave me an appreciative nod. He then apologized gravely to Avarelli, who accepted it with equal gravity, and without any hint of criticism or recrimination. Those two giants were so equable, so resilient, so utterly confident in their own powers, that the tiny dent made by my little piece of bravado lasted no longer than it took to play the next board. They were soon back on top, and stayed there.

Towards the end of the tournament we found ourselves due to play Venezuela. I knew very little about their team, either from current hearsay or by past reputation, but when I glanced at the line-up and saw the name of David Berah, I realized that here was a bridge force to be reckoned with.

Standing at the entrance to the Open Room, a vast concourse thronged with hundreds of players and spectators, I found no difficulty in immediately spotting Berah. He is one of those people who manage to be larger than life. A full head of wavy white hair surmounts a Florentine face; the expression alternates between breezy smiles and pugnacious scowls. He moves swiftly and with the ease of a dancer. He has the faculty of being able to attract attention to himself without trying.

At the table, Berah is as artful as a barrel of monkeys, but he can be as profound as Erasmus on occasions. As I watched him, I thought: here is a man capable of winning the match on his own. And so it proved.

At half-time we had a slight lead. Towards the end of the second half, my partner and I had the feeling that although we'd given little away, neither had we gained much. The few remaining boards were going to be critical. And this one was:

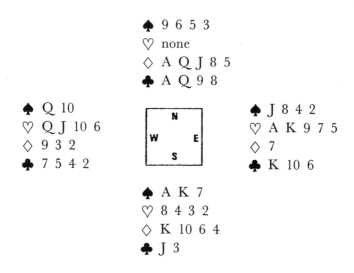

```
              ♠ 9 6 5 3
              ♡ none
              ◇ A Q J 8 5
              ♣ A Q 9 8
♠ Q 10                          ♠ J 8 4 2
♡ Q J 10 6          N           ♡ A K 9 7 5
◇ 9 3 2        W         E      ◇ 7
♣ 7 5 4 2           S           ♣ K 10 6
              ♠ A K 7
              ♡ 8 4 3 2
              ◇ K 10 6 4
              ♣ J 3
```

At game-all, East dealt, and produced a light 1 Heart opening. South passed, and West raised to 2 Hearts. North now doubled, and after a pass from East, South made the quite extraordinary bid of 4 Spades. It is not necessary to tell you that the South seat was occupied by David Berah, who cares little for the niceties of orthodox approach bidding.

After this bid was passed out, West led the Queen of Hearts, and Berah settled down to the task of justifying his flight of fancy by making 10 tricks. This is by no means an easy matter. If you touch trumps, you're finished. There is no obvious way to get home, but Berah is never daunted by the absence of the obvious.

He ruffed the Heart lead in dummy, led a Diamond to his King, and ruffed a second Heart. Now he led the 8 of Diamonds. East had bright hopes of a natural trump trick, and was not about to abandon it on what might be an abortive ruff. Instead he threw a Heart. The 10 of Diamonds won the trick, to the accompaniment of satanic chuckles from South.

A third Heart was ruffed in dummy, and Berah got off lead with a small Club, on which East pounced with his King. A much overdue trump was returned, won by the Ace, and the remaining cards looked like this:

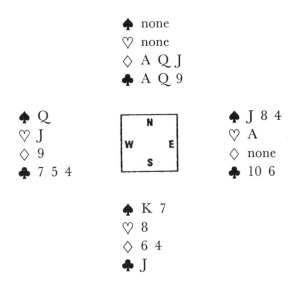

```
              ♠ none
              ♡ none
              ◇ A Q J
              ♣ A Q 9

♠ Q          ┌──N──┐        ♠ J 8 4
♡ J          │     │        ♡ A
◇ 9          W     E        ◇ none
♣ 7 5 4      │  S  │        ♣ 10 6
             └─────┘
              ♠ K 7
              ♡ 8
              ◇ 6 4
              ♣ J
```

Berah needed four more tricks. He took dummy's two top Clubs, discarding his last Heart, then led the Ace of Diamonds, which East had to ruff.

But now East found he had nowhere to go. If he forced Berah

with a Heart, the 7 of trumps would score. If he played a trump instead, the King would bring down West's Queen. A further Diamond would oblige East to relinquish his master trump by ruffing, and again the 7 of trumps would come into its own.

In the baffled silence which descended on the table after the hand was over, David Berah chattered away brightly in his broken English, giving no indication that either his bidding or his play was anything but routine. Perhaps, to him, that's what it was.

Monaco

Four years have passed. Many of the giants who bestrode their narrow world in the 1972 Olympiad have gone from the scene, their places taken by new faces with unfamiliar names. At Monaco in 1976, the Olympiad was infinitely more enjoyable as a total experience, but somehow less momentous, in that there seemed to be more ordinary mortals and fewer living legends.

But what a jewel of a place is little Monaco! Gentle, sunny, happy, carefree, a blessed haven of peace and sanity in a world going slowly mad. The atmosphere in which the matches took place was influenced to a large degree by the atmosphere in which the players basked in Monaco. Such pervasive serenity has its effects, and it was undoubtedly instrumental in producing the kind of relaxation that one dreams of but rarely finds in any kind of bridge tournament.

At the table there was a genuine friendliness, a willingness to overlook small inadvertent infractions, an easy tolerance which, while not abating by the least degree the competitive zeal of the players, made it possible to realize that this was a game taking place, and not a holy war.

186

As an illustration, let me take a tiny incident from our match against the Netherlands team. In the Open Room, a great baroque salon with acres of red velvet, heavily ornamented walls and ceiling, and a fine faded Edwardian elegance, small clusters of spectators grouped themselves around the players. We had a dozen or so in our gallery, attentive, respectfully silent, eagerly interested, craning forward to see the action. This was one of the hands they saw:

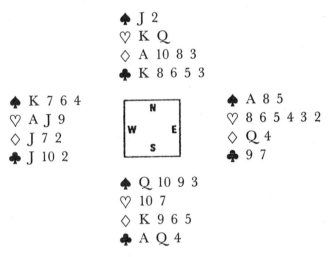

                    ♠ J 2
                    ♡ K Q
                    ◇ A 10 8 3
                    ♣ K 8 6 5 3

♠ K 7 6 4   ♠ A 8 5
♡ A J 9   ♡ 8 6 5 4 3 2
◇ J 7 2   ◇ Q 4
♣ J 10 2   ♣ 9 7

                    ♠ Q 10 9 3
                    ♡ 10 7
                    ◇ K 9 6 5
                    ♣ A Q 4

E–W were vul; South dealt. In the Closed Room, the Netherlands N–S pair stopped in 3 Diamonds and made 10 tricks. In the Open Room we bid it like this:

S	W	N	E
pass	pass	1 ♣	pass
1 NT	pass	2 ♣	pass
2 ♠	pass	2 NT	pass
3 NT	pass	pass	pass

After inching our way cautiously into a borderline game,

and having advertised a red suit weakness on the way there, all that West had to do was to pick the right red suit for his opening lead. But it is difficult to blame him for leading a Diamond instead of a Heart. The first trick consisted of the 2 of Diamonds followed by the 3, Q, and K.

In the South seat, I anxiously tried to assess my prospects. No point in making careless assumptions about a 3–2 split in Clubs at this stage; if I made 4 tricks in Diamonds and a Heart, I would still need a Spade trick to protect against a bad Club break. To test the Diamonds first, I led the 5 and finessed dummy's 10. Success. Now the Jack of Spades from dummy, on which everybody played low!

I couldn't resist glancing at the gallery, some of whom wore tell-tale grins. The contract was now safe, no matter what happened to the Clubs, so I decided to set up a Heart by playing the King. Again everybody played low! Now the grins turned to open smiles. Having prospected in three suits with surprising success, I now turned my attention to the Clubs, remarking aloud: "Better try this one next," and the gallery's pent-up amusement erupted into roars of laughter, in which our opponents freely joined.

I finished with two unexpected overtricks, but that is beside the point. The real point is that the prevailing psychological climate was so warm, tolerant and human, that my facetious remark, instead of being frowned on by a bunch of hyper-tense purists, or pounced on angrily by wrought-up opponents as unwarranted gamesmanship, seemed an entirely natural response to the situation, and was treated accordingly.

Our match against the cheerful Australian team was breathlessly close. From it comes this classic example of the importance of the spot cards. I occupied the West seat, opening a weak 2 ♡ as dealer and being raised to 4 ♡ by my partner:

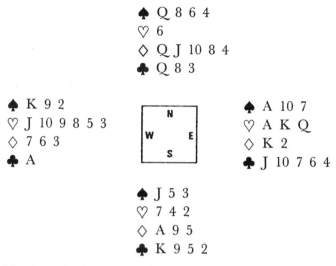

♠ Q 8 6 4
♡ 6
◇ Q J 10 8 4
♣ Q 8 3

♠ K 9 2
♡ J 10 9 8 5 3
◇ 7 6 3
♣ A

♠ A 10 7
♡ A K Q
◇ K 2
♣ J 10 7 6 4

♠ J 5 3
♡ 7 4 2
◇ A 9 5
♣ K 9 5 2

North made the only lead to give me a problem: a trump. On any other lead I should have no trouble in ruffing a Diamond in dummy for my 10th trick. So first a Club to the Ace, then a Diamond towards dummy in the hope that North held the Ace. But South won, and led another trump. Back in dummy again, I led the 2 of Diamonds. At this point, South must rise with the 9 to hold the trick and then destroy me with a third trump. But he played the 5, I covered, and poor trumpless North had to win.

Among all the tables at which this contract was played, only once was 4 ♡ defeated, no doubt because all the other North players found the "automatic" lead of the Queen of Diamonds, after which West has an easy ride.

My partner at Monaco for most of the matches was John Whillis, a native of Canada who plays a neat game. I should like to present an example of his workmanship as declarer on this far from easy hand in our match against Denmark. He sat South:

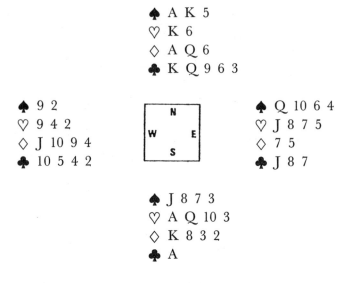

        ♠ A K 5
        ♡ K 6
        ◇ A Q 6
        ♣ K Q 9 6 3

♠ 9 2   ♠ Q 10 6 4
♡ 9 4 2   ♡ J 8 7 5
◇ J 10 9 4   ◇ 7 5
♣ 10 5 4 2   ♣ J 8 7

        ♠ J 8 7 3
        ♡ A Q 10 3
        ◇ K 8 3 2
        ♣ A

We had soared to a dizzy 7 NT, and West led a sly 9 of Diamonds. With only 11 tricks on top (15 South players actually went 2 down in 7 NT) a certain amount of careful thought and planning was needed.

Dummy's Ace won the opening lead, then a Club to the Ace, and back to dummy's other Diamond honor. Now came the King of Hearts, and Whillis then took the finesse of the 10. He opened his eyes and uncrossed his fingers to find that the 10 had stood up. So now the other two Hearts, then the Ace of Spades and the King and Queen of Clubs, which gave him as accurate a count on the hand as he could get in the circumstances. The end position was:

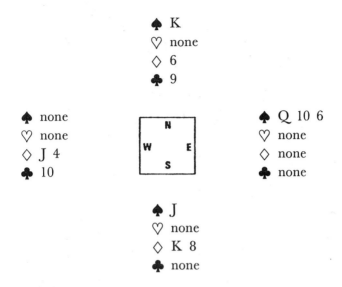

```
           ♠ K
           ♡ none
           ◇ 6
           ♣ 9

♠ none      ┌───────┐      ♠ Q 10 6
♡ none      │   N   │      ♡ none
◇ J 4       │ W   E │      ◇ none
♣ 10        │   S   │      ♣ none
            └───────┘
           ♠ J
           ♡ none
           ◇ K 8
           ♣ none
```

The play of the King of Spades squeezed West in the minors, and the grand slam rolled majestically into harbor. Whillis rang up "stop engines," let go of the helm, blew out a great quantity of breath, then lit a cigarette at the wrong end.